NATURAL RESOURCES FOR U.S. GROWTH

A Look Ahead to the Year 2000

NATURAL RESOURCES FOR U.S. GROWTH

A Look Ahead to the Year 2000

By Hans H. Landsberg

Based on the Resources for the Future study
Resources in America's Future,
by Hans H. Landsberg, Leonard L. Fischman, and
Joseph L. Fisher

PUBLISHED FOR *Resources for the Future, Inc.*
BY *The Johns Hopkins Press, Baltimore*

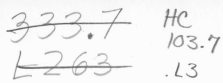

Preface

This examination of the adequacy of natural resources in the United States over the rest of the century is based on a much more detailed study—*Resources in America's Future: Patterns of Requirements and Availabilities, 1960-2000,* by Hans H. Landsberg, Leonard L. Fischman, and Joseph L. Fisher—published for Resources for the Future, Inc., by The Johns Hopkins Press.

In the parent study, the authors presented a comprehensive and systematic set of projections of future demand for resources and resource products, considered the possibilities of meeting such demands, and noted the major issues of policy implied by the conclusions. The work was backed up by a statistical appendix of nearly 500 pages—almost half the length of the entire book.

In this briefer, simpler form, RFF hopes to make available to students and general readers the reasoning, conclusions, and policy implications of the larger work. Condensation has been achieved by dropping the entire statistical appendix, and omitting or foreshortening many of the details of the analysis of requirements and supplies for particular commodities. But the essentials have been retained.

The present text was written by Hans H. Landsberg, principal author of the larger work, with the editorial assistance of Merle Colby. Illustrations were under the direction of Elmer E. Smith. He drew most of the charts and adapted the others from those designed by Clare O'Gorman Ford for *Resources in America's Future.*

I hope that this simplified, popularly priced version will meet the desire of many Americans to know more about their country's present capabilities and its prospects for future growth, in the light of natural resource adequacy. Here are discussed, with tentative answers where possible, questions asked by businessmen interested in projected future demand for consumer goods and services, intermediate products, and raw materials; by government legislators and administrators charged with shaping or carrying out U.S. resource policies; by community planners and area developers; by adult groups concerned with current social and political issues; and by college and upper high school teachers and students. Scholars primarily interested in method, and specialists seeking details on particular products will need to consult the original study.

JOSEPH L. FISHER, President
Resources for the Future, Inc.

Contents

Author's Note

In compressing the more detailed study, it was possible to preserve the findings only by shortening those portions of the text that present the reasoning for proceeding in one way rather than in another, the implications of the methodology, and the critique of the available statistics. As a result, the findings carry a flavor of greater certainty than they merit.

"Currently," "at present," "now," and similar terms refer to 1960, unless qualified. The research phase of the parent study was essentially closed in early 1962, and events in the two intervening years have not, for the sake of preserving comparability, been allowed to affect the text of this book. Where there was a compelling necessity to break this rule and update, this has been specifically noted. There are few such instances. For any unintended discrepancy between this book and the parent study, my co-authors bear no responsibility.

April, 1964

HANS H. LANDSBERG

1

Natural Resources
in the Economy

To inquire, as we do in this study, into the future adequacy of natural resources in the United States is to explore questions that will bear directly on the private life of every American, on the shape of the total economy, and on the nation's position of world leadership.

At first glance, this may seem too broad a claim. Science and technology are more and more making it possible to obtain needed goods and services from the most unlikely raw materials: society is not nearly so dependent on this particular acre or that ore as it used to be. And, partly as a result of these advances, the resource industries, like farming and mining, represent a smaller and smaller share of the entire economy. Only a tenth of the working population is needed for such tasks today; less than a century ago half the labor force was so employed.

But, fundamentally, natural resources are as important to the nation's survival and welfare as they ever were. Land and its products, water, mineral fuels, and the nonfuel minerals still are the indispensable physical stuff that provides the material basis of modern civilization. Indeed, in those uses that serve recreation and the enjoyment of beauty the contributions of land and water are far more than material.

The fact that nine-tenths of the working force is able to do other things than provide raw materials suggests the magnitude and variety of the structure that now rests on the base of natural resources: manufacturing, marketing, government,

1

education, national defense, the arts and sciences, recreation, and the many other aspects of modern society.

Vast amounts of resource products are needed to keep these activities going. While the *relative* importance of resource industries has diminished over the years, the *absolute* volume of resource production and consumption has been steadily increasing. The United States is by far the world's largest user of raw materials.

In 1952 the President's Materials Policy Commission noted with some awe that consumption of most of the fuels and other minerals in this country alone had been greater since the beginning of the First World War than total world consumption for all the preceding centuries. The national appetite for resource materials has grown greatly since then. In 1960 the United States used 80 million tons of metals (measured in their steel equivalent), 45 quadrillion Btu of energy (the equivalent of 1¾ billion tons of coal or of around 8 billion barrels of oil), 11.5 billion cubic feet of timber, and nearly $21 billion worth of farm products; and dissipated 85 billion gallons per day of the fresh water withdrawn from lakes and streams.

Those were the resource requirements of a nation of 180 million. For the year 2000, population is projected at around 330 million. In any case, a much larger number of people will want an even higher level of living than the average of today: better diets, better housing, more automobiles and consumer goods of all kinds, better educational and cultural opportunities, more facilities for outdoor recreation, and more of many other things. At the same time, they will want to maintain a strong defense establishment, and to continue to explore outer space and to provide assistance to less-developed countries.

Can the United States over the balance of the twentieth century count on enough natural resource supplies to support a rate of economic growth sufficient to fulfill all of these aspirations?

This is the central question behind Resources for the Future's inquiry into the future domestic requirements of natural resources and the products and services derived from them, and into the prospects of meeting such requirements. The study stops with the present century only because that seems as far as social scientists can profitably look ahead; uncertainties multiply with each decade into the future. The year 2000 will not bring an end to the importance of natural resources or the intensity of resource problems.

Defining the Question

Just what is the problem of resource adequacy? A century and a half ago, when Thomas Robert Malthus advanced the proposition that the unchecked growth of population inevitably would press upon the earth's limited supply of natural resources, the fear that preyed upon people's minds was of literal, physical scarcity. The English clergyman was thinking almost entirely of farm production in his own country, but the implications for all natural resource products became clear to many thinking people in the Western world. A few years later, David Ricardo, who considered mineral production as well as agriculture, modified the doctrine of scarcity by maintaining that the real threat was one of progressive decline of resource quality because the richest farmland and beds of ore would be used first. But even without ultimate limits, physical scarcity lay at the end of the road.

Physical scarcity still was the chief preoccupation early in the present century, when the First Conservation Movement was at its height in the United States. Many of the technical papers filed at Theodore Roosevelt's Governors' Conference of 1908 gave estimates of finite amounts of coal, iron, and other minerals in the United States, and calculated the dates when they would be exhausted.

None of these gloomy predictions has as yet been borne out. In the United States and the rest of the Western world there have been no large-scale examples of Malthusian scarcity, although there have been numerous temporary shortages of particular raw materials. One reason for the escape (or is it only a reprieve?) has been the rise in world trade; the early theories of scarcity presupposed a large degree of national self-sufficiency. Another, and more powerful, reason has been the widespread advance in technology. There are new ways of finding mineral deposits and mining those once thought inaccessible. Improved plant breeding and increased use of fertilizers have greatly raised crop yields. Better ways of processing and using raw materials have stretched the usefulness of a given quantity.

For these and other reasons, productivity in the U.S. resource industries has risen sharply. Although the working force in those lines (about 7 million) is no larger than it was ninety years ago, it turned out about five times as much in 1960 as in 1870. Finally, the possibilities of substituting one raw material for another have been enormously expanded, not only through new ways of using familiar materials but also through discovering some new materials in nature or of synthesizing others.

Nevertheless, the basic problem remains: How long can the natural resources of a finite world support growing populations at rising levels of living? Obviously there are physical limits to land surface; to amounts of fresh water moving through the hydrologic cycle, from ocean to cloud to rainfall to watercourses and back to the sea; and to mineral fuels and metallic ores. At certain times and in certain places such limitations have made themselves felt. This has not happened on any large scale, however, at least in the United States and most of the rest of the Western world. Physical limits on resources are more a philosophic concept than a practical barrier. No one knows how many mineral deposits are yet to be discovered, how much new land can be made suitable for agriculture or old land more productive, nor the degree to which fresh water supplies can be reused with comfort and safety. In recent years, especially since the pioneering report of the President's Materials Policy Commission, scarcity has been thought of more in terms of cost than of physically running out.

The degree of economic scarcity varies not only with the intensity of demand for resource products but also with the technology of exploiting them or developing substitutes. The early frontier farmer, hemmed in by forests and trying to work a field full of stones with a crude plow, was probably not impressed by superabundance of cropland. The limits of economic scarcity have been pushed back in step with the growth in demand—and sometimes even faster.

There is abundant oil in the shales and tar sands of the North American continent; abundant aluminum in the crust of the earth everywhere; abundant manganese and other metals in the nodules that cover much of the ocean floor; abundant timber in virtually untapped tropical forests. The crucial question usually is not how much there is of needed resource materials, but what it will cost to extract and put them to use.

While this new viewpoint modifies the problem of scarcity, it by no means solves it. If the costs of obtaining scarce natural resource products, or of developing substitutes for them, should rise significantly in relation to other costs, society would be devoting larger shares of manpower and capital to their production. At best, rising real cost would be a drag on the continued improvement in average levels of living; it could halt, or even reverse, the upward trend of recent decades.

In Search of Answers

The basic question addressed here, then, is this: Can the United States between now and the year 2000 obtain all the natural resources and resource products it needs at no significant increase in relative cost? More specifically, do any particular groups of products seem likely to present any special problems and, if so, what are the best ways of getting around the difficulties?

These are large questions. How could a comparatively small group of social scientists look ahead four decades in the broad and complicated field of natural resources and come out with useful answers? They could not, of course, foretell the future, and did not try. Instead, they analyzed the record of the past and the strength and direction of current trends, and asked what would happen if future developments should follow the pattern that seemed most likely at the start of the 1960's. To sum it all up in one word, they used projections.

A projection is a determination of what the future course of some statistical measure (annual copper production, for instance, or average income per family) would be under a certain set of starting assumptions. The assumptions, broad or narrow, daring or cautious, always determine the result.

Projections never are predictions of what is actually going to happen in the wide world of reality. Yet, if skillfully made, they can be far more than theoretical exercises; they can show implications of present trends and programs, and provide a benchmark for appraising later events as they actually do occur.

In projecting future resource needs and supplies in the United States, it was necessary first of all to have a working idea of what the nation's economy and society at large might be like in the year 2000 and along the way. What would the broad picture be if current trends, as modified by already discernible patterns of change, remain in operation? Three basic assumptions, built in from the start, were: continuing gains in technology, improvements in political and social arrangements, and a reasonably free flow of world trade. Two other assumptions on which the whole system of projections rests are that there will be neither a large-scale war nor a widespread economic depression like that of the early 1930's. Because the projections were based so firmly on historical statistics, it was not feasible to include Alaska and Hawaii in the detailed calculations though some data on Alaska are included in the discussion of forest products.

The starting point of the calculations was the handful of over-all factors like population, labor force, and gross national product that generally indicate the size and shape of the national economy. Then, within the limits of the total economy, levels of demand could be calculated for the large categories of human needs and wants—food, clothing, shelter, heat and power, transportation, durable goods of all sorts, military equipment, outdoor recreation and other identifiable requirements of an advanced industrial society. Requirements for specific resources did not as a general rule enter the picture at this stage. Unless they encounter noticeable price penalties, few consumers—whether individuals or industries—care what particular resource products are drawn upon so long as they have the goods and services they want.

Next, and with much thought to the possibilities of substitution and technological change, these requirements for end products were translated into requirements for such resource products as agricultural raw materials, steel, lumber, textile fibers, and the like. From these, in turn, the converging demands on land, water, fuels, and other minerals were estimated.* Figure 1 illustrates the projection process in diagram form. Finally, these projected demands were considered in relation to availability of supply. The estimates of future availability, though generally not as elaborately worked out as the requirements projections, rest on careful analysis of evidence now at hand on the basic resources of land, water, and min-

---

* In the large study nearly all projections were made at three levels— low, medium, and high—not only at the final stage but in most of the preliminary stages as well, starting with population. This was done to discover where different basic assumptions might lead in various combinations. If even the low projection of demand indicates pressure on a certain resource product, problems of adequacy are almost certain to arise. If the high projection reveals no pressure on supply it is equally likely that there is no problem. All three levels of assumption are quite within reason, but the middle levels are considered most likely. Unless specially designated, the medium projections are the only ones cited in this book.

Figure 1. Resources and economic growth:
how the demand projections were built up.

The chart illustrates successive steps in projecting demand for a few selected products. Starting with projections of population, labor force, households, and gross national product at the top, the diagram traces, as one reads down (1) the estimated demands for goods and services, (2) the resulting requirements for key materials, and (3) the demand for basic resources and resource products of which there are many more than those shown on the bottom line. The chart also suggests the way in which different elements in the economy combine to create the level of demand for particular products. The chart does not attempt to show all the cross-relationships involved, even for the handful of items selected, and many intermediate stages also have been omitted.

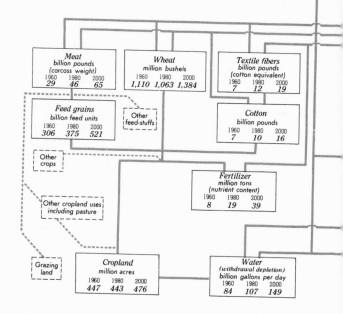

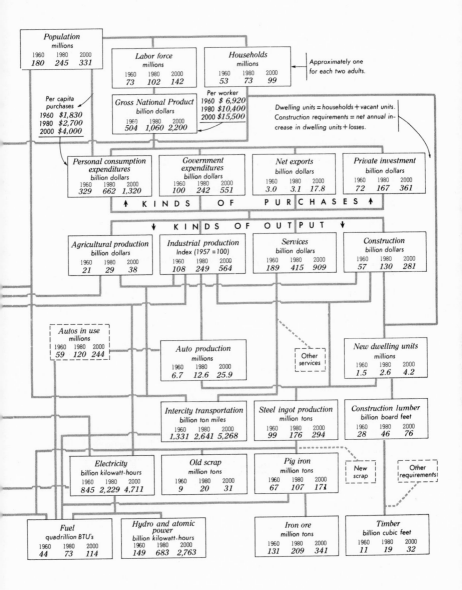

Population
millions

1960	1980	2000
180	*245*	*331*

Labor force
millions

1960	1980	2000
73	*102*	*142*

Households
millions

1960	1980	2000
53	*73*	*99*

Approximately one
for each two adults.

**Per capita
purchases**

1960	*$1,830*
1980	*$2,700*
2000	*$4,000*

Gross National Product
billion dollars

1960	1980	2000
504	*1,060*	*2,200*

Per worker
1960 $ 6,920
1980 $10,400
2000 $15,500

Dwelling units = households + vacant units.
Construction requirements = net annual increase in dwelling units + losses.

**Personal consumption
expenditures**
billion dollars

1960	1980	2000
329	*662*	*1,320*

**Government
expenditures**
billion dollars

1960	1980	2000
100	*242*	*551*

Net exports
billion dollars

1960	1980	2000
3.0	*3.1*	*17.8*

Private investment
billion dollars

1960	1980	2000
72	*167*	*361*

↑ K I N D S   O F   P U R C H A S E S ↑

↓ K I N D S   O F   O U T P U T ↓

Agricultural production
billion dollars

1960	1980	2000
21	*29*	*38*

Industrial production
Index (1957 = 100)

1960	1980	2000
108	*249*	*564*

Services
billion dollars

1960	1980	2000
189	*415*	*909*

Construction
billion dollars

1960	1980	2000
57	*130*	*281*

Autos in use
millions

1960	1980	2000
59	*120*	*244*

Auto production
millions

1960	1980	2000
6.7	*12.6*	*25.9*

Other
services

New dwelling units
millions

1960	1980	2000
1.5	*2.6*	*4.2*

Intercity transportation
billion ton miles

1960	1980	2000
1,331	*2,641*	*5,268*

Steel ingot production
million tons

1960	1980	2000
99	*176*	*294*

Construction lumber
billion board feet

1960	1980	2000
28	*46*	*76*

Electricity
billion kilowatt-hours

1960	1980	2000
845	*2,229*	*4,711*

Old scrap
million tons

1960	1980	2000
9	*20*	*31*

Pig iron
million tons

1960	1980	2000
67	*107*	*171*

New
scrap

Other
requirements

Fuel
quadrillion BTU's

1960	1980	2000
44	*73*	*114*

**Hydro and atomic
power**
billion kilowatt-hours

1960	1980	2000
149	*683*	*2,763*

Iron ore
million tons

1960	1980	2000
131	*209*	*341*

Timber
billion cubic feet

1960	1980	2000
11	*19*	*32*

erals and the technology of getting goods and services from them. The possibility that large deposits are still undiscovered adds to the uncertainties for mineral fuels and metals.

The resource appraisal was made on a comprehensive basis. A common body of assumptions and basic projections of population and GNP underlies the whole study and keeps the projections for particular consumer needs and particular resource demands consistent with the outlook for the entire economy. For instance, metals, lumber, and cement compete as structural materials; projected use of any one affects the projections for the other two. Because all goods and services compete for the consumer's dollar, only an over-all constraint on total projected expenditure can keep the sum of the parts from exceeding the whole.

Reasonably possible advances in technology have been taken into account whenever their form could be envisaged and their likely consequences estimated. This is not common practice; in many projections, because of the multitude of uncertainties, no allowance is made for technological change. But in striving for the closest possible appreciation of the future, it has seemed better to guess, even on slender evidence, than to ignore. A footloose speculation four decades ago about dieselization of the railroads would have yielded a better projection of future coal and oil demand than one based on the assumption that locomotives would forever carry boilers.

No major changes in future price relationships have been assumed beyond those that may be implicit in past and current consumption trends. That is, estimates of future supply conditions have not been allowed to affect projections of requirements. This is clearly unrealistic, unlike the other major assumptions, particularly that of continued technological advance. As a product becomes scarcer or more plentiful, changes in relative cost and price surely will occur. Higher prices will tend to reduce demand, often through encouraging substitute products. Lower relative prices will usually stimulate demand, and sometimes discourage production as well. In either case, supply and demand would be brought closer together. This one departure from realism was deliberate. The main purpose of the whole study was to test adequacy of resource supplies to meet the demands as projected without substantial changes in price relationships, not to cover up possible future trouble spots by assuming that market action will take care of them.

A nearer target date than the year 2000 would have been safer, because the uncertainties multiply as projection is extended. But it is not so useful if the aim is to uncover possible future problems in time for people to do something about them. For example, if one cast forward only to 1980 he might conclude that the United States would not run into supply difficulties for the conventional fuels. But even a general idea of what may happen in the two following decades suggests that the nation has done well not to wait until then to begin developing nuclear power and the technology for using new sources of liquid fuels. Many long-term resource investment decisions that will affect the economy and the face of the land for many decades—dams, for instance, or the launching of new conservation programs—will have to be made in the next few years.

The Broad Conclusions

The projections indicate great increases in U.S. needs for natural resources and resource products: a tripling of requirements for both energy and metals by the year 2000, almost a tripling for timber, and almost a doubling for farm products and for withdrawal depletions of fresh water. (See Figure 2.) Other important and fast-growing uses of water, such as recreation and dilution of wastes, cannot as yet be statistically measured with the same degree of confidence, if at all.

Will these unprecedented amounts be forthcoming? The answer is a qualified yes. With due regard to the requirements

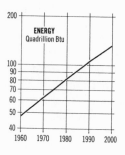

The increases in domestic requirements shown here are those that would occur between 1960 and 2000 under what seem to be the most likely assumptions of population, gross national product, technological progress and other key factors that will govern demand. They are projections, not predictions, for no one can tell in advance whether all or any of the underlying assumptions will be borne out. They do, however, show the direction in which things will be heading if most of the current major trends continue.

Metals represented are iron and steel, manganese, aluminum, copper, lead, and zinc. Their combined growth is shown on a common basis of steel equivalent, a measure of volume determined by specific gravity.

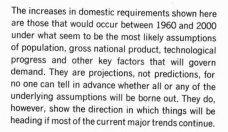

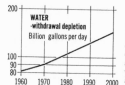

Withdrawal depletions represent actual losses sustained during use; that is, the difference between total withdrawals and amounts of withdrawn water later returned to lakes and streams. This measure does not include flows of fresh water required to prevent excessive pollution in watercourses, a requirement which in many areas is growing faster than withdrawal depletions.

"Roundwood" represents logs and other round sections as cut from trees before the bark is removed.

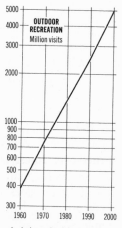

Includes only visits to principal kinds of public recreation areas — national parks, monuments, and recreation areas; state parks; and national forests.

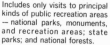

Figure 2. Growing U.S. needs for natural resource goods and services.

of other countries, the indications are that the American people *can* obtain the natural resources and resource products that they will need between now and the year 2000. Whether or not they *will* depends on how hard and how well they work at it.

Neither a long view of the past, nor current trends, nor our most careful estimates of future possibilities suggest any general running out of resources in this country during the remainder of this century. The possibilities of using lower grades of raw material, of substituting plentiful materials for scarce ones, of getting more use out of given amounts, of importing some things from other countries, and of making multiple use of land and water resources seem to be sufficient guarantee against across-the-board shortage.

This does not exclude problems of shortage (or, as in the case of agriculture during the next decade or two, of surplus) from time to time in particular segments of the economy, for particular raw materials. Deficiencies either of quantity or quality in the environmental resources of land and water undoubtedly will also occur in some instances.

Problems of quality, touched on only briefly in the study, are just as important as the problems of quantity and probably more difficult. Simply having enough oil, metals, land, and water would not spell a satisfactory life for most people. For example, there is surely enough land for urban expansion for many years to come and probably for outdoor recreation also, but the quality of it could be allowed to deteriorate to the point where it would yield unsatisfactory services. Similarly, burned-over forest land and abandoned strip mines lie ugly and useless for many years unless treated and restored. Pollution of water does not usually prevent its use, but it does make use less pleasant and more costly. The relationship of people to resources, which usually has been expressed in terms of quantity, needs to be restated for modern times to emphasize what is happening to the quality of resources.

These major findings are quite generalized and in the

original study are highly qualified as well. Furthermore, most
—probably all—of the numerical projections will turn out to
be more or less wide of the mark as the future unfolds. Was
it worthwhile to make so painstaking a study to get such
results? Those of us who made the parent study thought
so, for the inevitable limitations were foreseen from the start.
The findings do show where the nation stands with regard to
natural resources and where it seems to be heading. The study
supplies the background information on coming issues in
time for people to weigh the evidence and arrive at appropriate public and private decisions. And the detail behind the
broad conclusions points up the specific problems for individual resources and resource products.

The rest of this book deals with some of these details.
Chapter 2 looks briefly at the broad prospects for the economy
as a whole. Chapter 3 considers future requirements for living
and what they appear to mean in terms of needs for the
various natural resources and their products. Chapter 4 considers the availability of resources to meet the projected requirements. Finally, Chapter 5 reviews some of the chief
policy issues suggested by the findings and the basic assumptions behind them. For although this is not primarily a study
of resources policy, its main purpose is to present facts that
will contribute to intelligent and timely policy decisions.

2

The Size and Shape
of the Future Economy

The best guide to future requirements for natural resources and resource products appears to be, as already noted in Chapter 1, the projected pattern of demand for broad categories of human wants and needs like food, clothing, shelter and other construction, transportation, heat and power and half a dozen others. When these demands have been estimated, one can then go on to estimate the amounts of resources or resource materials that each would call for, fully realizing, of course, that the many uncertainties involved—especially the opportunity for substituting one material for another and other facets of modern technology—will make the most careful answer only a rough approximation.

But before one can project the broad categories of demand, it is necessary to have a general idea of what the U.S. economy will be like between now and the year 2000, above all, the number of people and their average level of prosperity. This calls for further projections, which might for the purposes of this study be thought of as basic assumptions. These we shall examine first.

The more detailed projections that come later in this chapter are based on a uniform set of assumptions and projections about the nation's future economy. Most fundamental of all are the projections of population, which will determine numbers of households and individual consumers, and projections of levels of income and economic activity, which will help determine how much people will be able to buy and how much can be made available. Population enters into the second kind of projections too, as the key factor in the size of the labor force. Another across-the-board element is the expectation of continued progress in technology; the specific direction of such advances, however, and their possible rates of adoption have to be considered separately in each case.

Population

The United States is likely to have a population of around 245 million in 1980 and around 330 million in the year 2000, as compared with 180 million in 1960. These figures, like almost all population projections, are based on studies of the U.S. Bureau of the Census. The growth expected during the rest of the century is equivalent to an annual increase of about 1.55 per cent. This is substantially higher than the growth rate between 1920 and 1940, but is slightly below the rate that prevailed in 1940-60, a period which included the post-war "baby boom." It is also lower than any 20-year or 40-year rate preceding 1920, for it is difficult to imagine ever again a rate of immigration such as prevailed prior to World War I.

The principal factor of uncertainty in population projections has for some time been the fertility rate. To the distress of population forecasters, the American birth rate has been subject to substantial changes in direction. In this country at least, most modern population forecasts that have gone awry have done so because they assumed continuation of whatever trend in fertility was evident when the estimates were made. Although demographers have learned to identify the different elements which must be considered in making population projections, they cannot weigh the future decisions of young married couples as to the number of children they will have. For example, the years of high birth rates in this country immediately following World War II were, with much plausibility, believed to be a temporary phenomenon following the war years. Instead, these high rates have persisted, thus upsetting all projections made in the late forties and early fifties.

The projections used here are predicated on a gradual decrease in fertility rate and not much change in mortality or net immigration. Since the size of the population is vital to a large number of resource demand projections, it follows that any deviation in actual fact from that assumed here will affect a great many of the projections. The uncertainty introduced by possible variations in the fertility rate is by no means small. If higher or lower (but still perfectly possible) rates are substituted, the population projection for the year 2000 goes as high as 430 million or as low as 270 million, instead of the 330 million which has been chosen as the most likely population for that year. (See Figure 3, which also shows projections for households and labor force, both discussed below.)

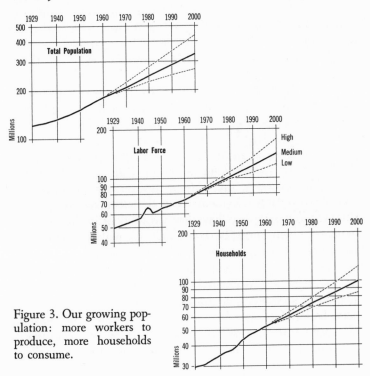

Figure 3. Our growing population: more workers to produce, more households to consume.

For some purposes, notably house building, it is more important to have an idea of the number of households than the number of individual people. In turn, it is essential to project the number of houses or dwelling units in order to make estimates of house heating, appliance use, etc.

Gross National Product

The most inclusive measure of the economic performance of the nation—the gross national product—can be projected in different ways. One way is to look at the past development and calculate from it the growth rate of the economy. One can then assume that the future will not be substantially different from the past and, using a historical rate, project the GNP from its 1960 base.

Here we follow a somewhat different procedure. Since the nation cannot produce more goods and services than the size and productivity of its labor force will permit, separate projections have been made of these two elements, with GNP derived as the product of the two.

In 1960 nearly 58 per cent of the 127 million people of 14 years or over were in the labor force—either actually employed or looking for work. This rate of participation is not expected to vary more than a fraction of a percentage point during the rest of the century, not because there will be no changes but because conflicting trends will about cancel each other out. Young people of both sexes will tend to stay in school longer and more older workers will take advantage of opportunities to retire. But the proportion of women in their thirties or forties entering or re-entering the labor market will rise sharply from the 1960 level of 40 per cent or less. Thus, the labor force is expected to increase roughly in proportion to total population. This would mean 140 million workers by the year 2000, almost double the 1960 figure.

As for productivity, there is no evidence at this time to show that we are at the threshold of a significant long-term rise in the man-hour productivity rate for the economy as a whole, in spite of much speculation about the future spillover from new technology in the military and space field to ordinary civilian uses and recent spurts in industrial productivity. The declining importance of agriculture in which labor productivity has increased spectacularly, and the growing importance of services in which there has been no measurable increase might make one argue, instead, that productivity increases will be smaller in the future than in the past.

Because GNP is not only a measure of output, but also the sum total of what consumers, business, and government jointly spend, an independent estimate has been made of what GNP ought to be on a spending basis, that is, regardless of the size of the labor force and the rate of productivity. By balancing the results of this approach against the other, one can be reasonably sure that both estimates make sense, or at least that they are consistent. The rate of growth in GNP that emerges from these calculations is not quite 3.8 per cent per year between now and the end of the century. (See Figure 4.) This—a doubling every twenty years—is better than we have done in recent years, not as well as we have done at some points in the past, and certainly less well than many would like us to do in the future.

Why is it important to project the size of GNP? Since we are ultimately interested in the demand for natural resources, why bother with a measure which is a conglomerate of all goods and services?

One answer is that we do have an interest in gauging the future development of GNP for its own sake, as a broad indicator of the rate of development of the economy as a whole. Projection of GNP also provides a starting point for a good many other statistical projections more directly related to the demand for natural resources. Many of the statistical series developed in order to arrive at demand projections for natural resources can best be estimated by relating them to GNP. Since the margins within which long-term projections of GNP can vary are not too wide, they provide a fairly

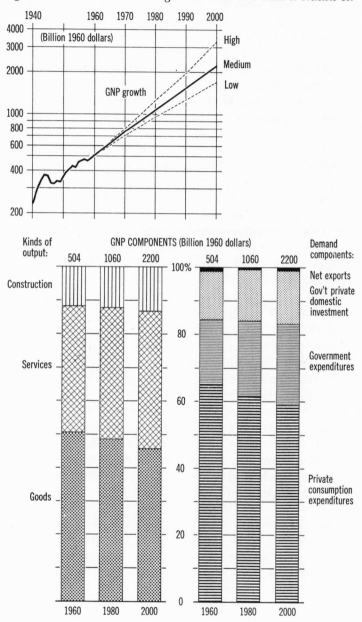

Figure 4. Measure of economic growth: GNP and what it consists of.

reasonable base from which to project other series, provided one remains alert to possible developments that may upset past relationships. Up to now, the relationships between GNP and a great many other economic series have been remarkably consistent. Thus one may utilize GNP and its principal components as part of a broad framework for estimating consumption of the various kinds of goods and the size of future material and resource requirements.

Individual Spending

Personal consumption expenditures are a major component of GNP and a stepping-stone toward estimating the demand for any number of final and intermediate commodities that together make up the broad category of "requirements for living." By projecting per capita expenditure patterns of today into the future, largely on the basis of how these expenditure patterns have varied in the past but partly on the basis of likely future changes that do not necessarily emerge from the record of the past, one can project monetary demand for various kinds of goods and services.

In the early 1960's, personal consumption expenditures amount to around two-thirds of GNP. This compares to about four-fifths at the beginning of the 1900's, and three-quarters in the 1920's. This decline in individual spending is balanced by the increase in government expenditures, not only for defense but also for any number of community services—education, general health, security, etc.—that the individual does not buy in the marketplace. The proportion of personal consumption expenditures to GNP is not projected to decline much further; it is expected to yield only a few more percentage points to increased expenditures by government.

These expectations of decline are, of course, only relative, as individual standards of living rise. The absolute amounts of per capita consumer expenditure are projected to increase by almost 50 per cent in the next twenty years, and more than

100 per cent by the end of the century. Different types of consumer expenditures will grow at different rates. The largest expenditures today are for food, shelter, and clothing. Food and shelter are likely to stay at the top of the list, even though there seems to be long-range decline in the proportion of the total consumer budget spent for food. Expenditures for housing, on the other hand, are expected to grow at about the same rate as total consumer expenditures. Some categories of expenditure will grow more than proportionately. Household appliances, furniture, recreation—including everything from golfing to foreign travel—and other items often described

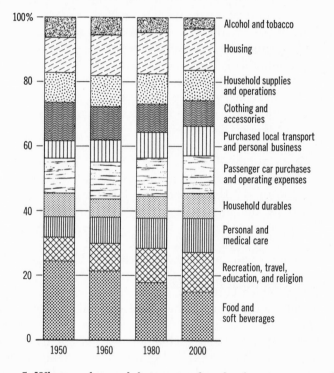

Figure 5. What people spend their money for: the changing pattern of personal consumption.

as "discretionary spending" are in this growing group. Figure 5 gives some indication of the changes projected for the different types of consumer expenditure.

Government Spending

Whether one welcomes or deplores the fact, there is little reason to doubt that government spending at all levels will be increased. The projected rise is moderate, however: from today's 20 per cent of GNP to 25 per cent at the end of the century. This, of course, includes the defense segment, which is assumed to remain a constant percentage of GNP. In absolute magnitude, defense expenditures would therefore increase year after year, reaching something like four times today's level by the end of the century. However, all space exploration is included in the defense projections.

Business Investment

Private investment has been projected to remain at around 15 per cent of total GNP, the proportion it has maintained during the last decade. That is, it is expected to rise just about as fast as GNP itself. The 15 per cent figure was not estimated as a residual (after personal and government expenditures had been determined), but was built up from separate projections of the main components of investment: new construction, producers' plant and equipment, and inventories. (See Figure 6.)

Index of Industrial Production

An important clue to the economy of the future is given by the projections of the Federal Reserve Board Index of Industrial Production, the principal single measure of the country's industrial economy. There are many cross relationships between projections of this index and projections of demand for specific types of commodities and materials.

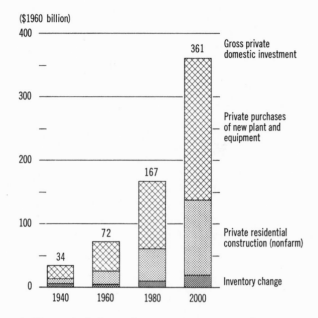

Figure 6. The outlook for total private investment and its components.

Many of the components of the index are either based on or are closely related to physical quantities such as tonnages consumed of a given material or tonnages produced of a given product. Quite frequently, therefore, components of the index have been projected in the light of past trends. Such indexes of future materials demand have been used in combination with materials demand derived in more direct fashion to get a better measure of the prospects. This procedure often modifies the original projections of the index. Hence, second, third, and fourth rounds of estimates have often been made to arrive at consistent movements of the index, its components, and materials production or demand.

Let us look at an example of this complex statistical process. The projected consumption of electric power by industry is based upon the past relationship (and the future relationship derived from the past) between the industrial production index as a whole and the consumption of energy in industry. Production of the primary sources of power—oil, gas, and coal—is itself an integral part of the index. Yet these quantities cannot very well be estimated without assuming beforehand how industry as a whole will develop in the future. At some point or other one must break into this closed circle. Here is how it is done: having derived a first estimate of total oil, coal, and gas consumption by making broad assumptions about the economy's growth in its various segments, including industrial consumption, one then goes back to the index of industrial production and inserts those physical amounts, thus refining the index. On a second round, using the index as refined, the relationship of the refined index to industrial energy consumption is estimated, resulting in amended projections of demand for coal, gas, and oil, etc. This is the statistical process of "iteration" in which, by successive approaches and rounds of calculation, different parts are made consistent with one another. (The past history of the index of industrial production, its projected future course, and the development of some of its major components are shown in Figure 7.)

Continued Advances in Technology

Technological change already has played a major role in resources adequacy. Characteristically this has taken the form of increased efficiency—getting more service or performance out of each unit of resources—and of widening the choice among resources. The pound of coal that was burned up in the course of generating one kilowatt-hour of electricity twenty years ago would produce over 1.5 kwh today.

Had corn yields been at the level of the forties, it would have taken nearly 100 million acres to produce the crop grown in 1962 on 57 million acres. Similar calculations in other resource fields would yield similarly striking illustrations.

The need to allow for technical change in considering

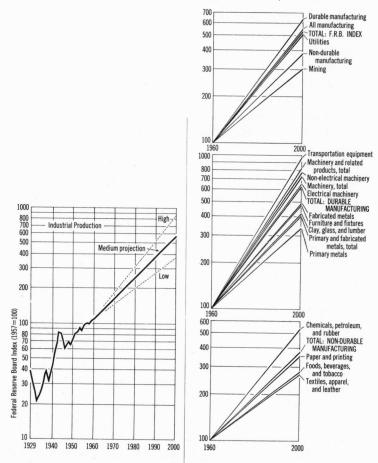

Figure 7. Rising industrial production: the over-all prospect and varied patterns of its components.

future resource adequacy is clear enough, but the statistical methods for putting this conviction to work are rough at best. Yet, it seems preferable to be vulnerable in the magnitude of the allowance made than to attempt no correction at all for future technological change.

Technological advances that will lead to improvements, modifications, and extensions of known and previously applied techniques and procedures have been assumed throughout the study. There are examples in all fields: increases in crop yields, and in efficiency of livestock production per animal; increasing use of electric power, but declining requirements for energy from all sources per unit of industrial output; increasing efficiency of conversion of heat to energy in conventional power generation; utilization of a larger portion of each tree felled and greater flexibility in choice of species in lumbering operations; a continuing trend toward alloyed metals combined with a decided preference for the lighter metals; further reductions of the share of materials in the value of much durable equipment, both in the consumer field and in industrial equipment; or further substitutions of man-made materials for natural substances, be they fibers, rubbers, films, drying oils, cleansing agents, and so forth.

For example, it has been assumed in the RFF projections that by the end of the century only 625 pounds of coal will have to be burned in electric utility plants to generate 1,000 kwh of electric power—down nearly 30 per cent from the 1960 level. While it may be taken for granted that this will not hit the nail on the head, it is even more certain that what may seem an arbitrary choice is preferable to assuming no change. Indeed, the effect of a "no change" assumption is staggering. Assuming coal, gas, and oil to be burned in the proportions estimated in the RFF projections, but at 1960 steam plant efficiencies, the additional fuel demand in the year 2000 would be more than 1,300 billion cubic feet of gas, plus 50 million barrels of oil, plus some 185 million tons of coal. (See Figure 8.) The hypothetical increments in that year would be equal to about three-fourths the gas, over 90 per cent of the coal and almost one-half the fuel oil now consumed annually in electric power generation.

No such allowances have been made statistically for innovations that represent radical departures in ways of doing

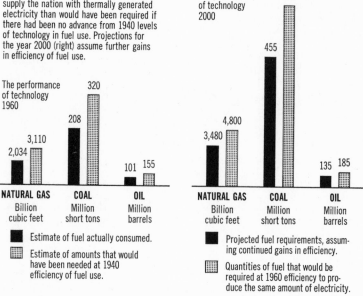

In 1960 (below) far less fuel was needed to supply the nation with thermally generated electricity than would have been required if there had been no advance from 1940 levels of technology in fuel use. Projections for the year 2000 (right) assume further gains in efficiency of fuel use.

The promise of technology 2000

The performance of technology 1960

320

208

3,110

2,034

101 155

640

455

4,800

3,480

135 185

NATURAL GAS   COAL   OIL
Billion   Million   Million
cubic feet   short tons   barrels

■ Estimate of fuel actually consumed.

▦ Estimate of amounts that would have been needed at 1940 efficiency of fuel use.

NATURAL GAS   COAL   OIL
Billion   Million   Million
cubic feet   short tons   barrels

■ Projected fuel requirements, assuming continued gains in efficiency.

▦ Quantities of fuel that would be required at 1960 efficiency to produce the same amount of electricity.

Figure 8. More kilowatt-hours per Btu: the influence of technological advance on fuel requirements for generating electricity.

things, and in the emergence of altogether new types of products and services. These limitations constitute perhaps the most serious weakness in any appraisal of resource adequacy.

It is difficult to find any single factor that exerts an influence upon resources demand comparable to that of technological change. For example, a "quantum jump" in genetics might permit a major degree of control over the conformation and characteristics of livestock or enable the agriculturist to extend to all major crops and to trees as well the advantages that he has reaped from the development of hybrid corn; a decisive advance in weather control could eliminate much of the chance factor in the raising of crops; a breakthrough in desalinization methods could make fresh water available to coastal areas and their hinterlands at such cost as to permit not only industrial but also agricultural operations; and the taming of the thermonuclear fusion process could provide a cheap source of energy without radioactive waste products, and one that would have fuel available into the indefinite future. These and many others are the types of development that one can think about, talk about, and list, but whose consequences cannot conscientiously be used in statistics. Any allowance for technological advance that one is able to build into adequacy projections is likely to be on the conservative side. The policy implications are equally plain: without strongly continuing technological advance our society would quickly run up against inconvenient and perhaps critical material limitations.

In the interest of brevity, the detailed projections of human needs and resource requirements that follow will be stated in this book with only a necessary minimum of qualifications and reservations. The reader is asked, however, to bear in mind the many assumptions behind the projections and the cautions that have been stated. Above all, he is urged not to regard *projections* to the year 1980 or 2000 as *predictions* of the way things will necessarily turn out.

3

Future Requirements

The projections of population and total economic activity that we have just considered in Chapter 2 can do no more than establish general guidelines to demand for natural resources and their products. Within those broad limits, future resource requirements will depend largely upon human needs and wants for a variety of resource-derived goods and services and upon the technologies by which they are made available.

In this chapter we examine the demands for food, clothing and other textiles, housing and other construction, heat and power, transportation, containers and packaging, paper for uses other than packaging and construction, and durable goods (consumer, producer, and military).

When taken together, the prospects in each of these large sectors are the best available clue to future demands for specific resources. Estimated total requirements for forest products, fuels, and metals are developed later in this chapter.

Although production of food, fiber, and timber accounts for most of the demand for land, no effort is made here to estimate a total requirement. This is because two of the fastest-growing uses of land—outdoor recreation and space for towns and cities—are not discussed until the next chapter, where projected demands for resources are compared with estimates of available supply. All discussion of needs for fresh water is reserved for that chapter.

The chief reasons for the many uncertainties that attend all projections of demand for particular resources are: (1) the increasing opportunity to substitute one material for another that technology has made possible, and (2) the growing importance of taste and fashion as rising levels of living enable a larger share of resources to be used for things people want rather than those they absolutely must have. Consequently, nearly all our forward estimates involve a large degree of judgment, a circumstance so inevitable that it requires no apology.

But this does not mean that one can only guess. Even with the certainty of rapid and unpredictable changes, there are main currents that change but slowly. This enables one to approximate future resource requirements under reasonable assumptions as to rate and character of growth and change. Some houses some place may soon be made solely of plastics; but not all houses everywhere. Some parts of some makes of automobiles may be made of aluminum, or plastic, but not all parts of all makes, and so on. In what follows, the likely consequences of rising incomes, changing preferences, and materials substitution have been taken into account but have been kept within bounds by being made consistent with our ideas of the general trend of the American economy.

PATTERNS OF FOOD USE

Food is of prime concern even in this richest of all nations. In one way or another the task of keeping people fed involves about 15 per cent of the productive activity of the United States economy. Of every dollar spent by the consumer, some 20 cents go for food, and food expenditures are thus an important determinant of demand for other goods and services. But in the context of this book, food is of interest most as a claimant of land, and more specifically of land suitable for raising crops or supporting pasture.

The per capita demand for food remains rather stable. Statistics suggest that throughout the first half of this century the average American consumer—average in the strictly statistical sense—has year after year consumed a little over 1,500

pounds of food, at retail weight. Only in the very recent past
has this amount dropped slightly. In terms of calories, consumption has declined more noticeably—from some 3,500
calories early in the century to just below 3,200 calories in the
past few years.

Of late, this trend is undoubtedly associated with a fear of
overweight and its well-publicized discomforts or worse. Other
factors, too, are operating to reduce food requirements: the
decreased amount of physical labor, improvements in house
heating, migration toward warmer climates, and, importantly,
population shifts toward a higher proportion of women, young
children, and old people. Most of these trends will continue,
with consequent further—though less substantial—declines
in per capita food consumption.

The Changing Menu

To provide one person with 3,200 calories a day for a year
would at present take just a little over half an acre if the
food were all in the form of bread, around two acres if it
were all milk, and more than 10 acres if it were all beef.
Clearly, food resource requirements cannot be calculated without close inquiry into today's and tomorrow's menus. For
example, it takes more feed and more acreage to raise 100
pounds of beef than 100 pounds of pork. In short, whether
Americans will eat more bread or more meat or more vegetables is not only a dietary question, but one that crucially
affects the requirements for acreage. Figure 9 shows how
different groups of foods have contributed to total food consumption in the past and compares the composition of today's
menus with those envisaged for the future. No estimate is
included for foods like coffee, tea, and cocoa, which make
no claim on domestic land resources.

Future developments in the consumption of specific foods
will depend upon changes in price relationships and income
levels, consumer tastes and preferences, and the relative
availability of different foods. But on the whole, the cheaper

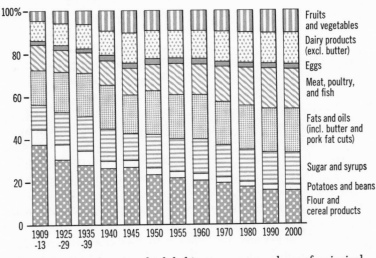

Figure 9. Our changing food habits: percentage share of principal food groups in total caloric consumption.

calorie sources such as cereal products and potatoes are giving way to the more expensive sources such as meats and, up to a point, fruits and vegetables.

The American public has become so responsive to the latest scientific findings, as brought to their attention through the mass media, that forward estimating in the food field has become hazardous. It is quite conceivable, for example, that the outcome of cholesterol research—still not removed from controversy—is likely to have a far greater bearing on future patterns of food consumption than variations in the price of butter or corn oil. Nonetheless, the basic roles of large food groups like meat, wheat, dairy products, etc., are less difficult to predict than the future of individual food items. Moreover, a continued desire for variety will set limits on the trends for particular foods.

Management practices and technological development, as well as individual preference, affect patterns of food use. In the three decades preceding World War II the level of poultry consumption did not change significantly. Suddenly per capita consumption started to rise; within the next 18 years it had doubled. This change was due in large part to the development of broiler production as a commercial enterprise. Today barely more than 10 per cent of all chickens are raised on the farm.

Modern broiler raising, characterized by high efficiency, above all in feed consumption, and helped by early determination of sex, which has made it possible for poultry farmers to specialize in egg production and leave the poultry meat trade to the broiler producers, has led to steeply falling prices and rising sales. Integration of growers with feed suppliers has led to even greater efficiency—so much so that American poultry-raising methods have spread to Western Europe and the term "broiler industry" has replaced "chicken farming."

The nutritive value of milk, its role in child feeding, and the effect of rising incomes are unlikely to keep per capita consumption of milk from continuing the decline that has characterized it for more than two decades. But in contrast with a 20 per cent drop between 1940 and 1960 less than a 10 per cent decline is envisaged through the end of the century. Both the past trend and the projection are the composite of two different developments: a decline in the use of the fat solids—or butterfat—and a rise in the consumption of nonfat solids. The inroads of cheaper fat substitutes, made possible by the gradual removal of legal restraints on the sale of oleomargarine and more recently reinforced by the public apprehension over the possible effects of a high-butterfat diet, have been important factors in this. As a consequence, milk producers have dropped their earlier goal of producing maximum butterfat and are now trying to maximize nonfat solids. So far the rising demand for nonfat solids has been met by diverting an increasing percentage from livestock to human consumption. The rising trend in nonfat solids has therefore not stemmed the decline in per capita milk consumption. When the demand for nonfat solids can no longer be met through diversion from feeding, it will overcome the depressing effect of the decline in butterfat consumption.

The decline in per capita wheat consumption is a striking example of the slow but steady change in dietary habits as incomes rise. Other factors in this decline are less waste in the use of flour, less spoilage of baked goods as the result of better packaging and use of preservatives, and the fact that commercial bakers have over the years greatly increased the amount of nonflour ingredients in their products. Taking all factors into account, per capita wheat consumption in the United States can be expected to decline from its 1960 rate of 165 pounds a year to a level of only 120 pounds, or nearly one-third less, by the end of the century.

Other food grains are of much less importance. Only a small fraction of total corn production is used for human consumption, and the demand for rye, barley and other grains for use as food is small in terms of acreage requirements.

No other foods are of so much importance in assessing the need for cropland acreage. When wheat and feed grains needed to provide livestock products are accounted for—as they are in Chapter 4—there need only be determined the requirements for oilseed crops, vegetables, and fruits.

In the case of oilseed, in some instances it is difficult to decide whether food or feed is the ruling use. Vegetables and fruits require only a very small acreage, but it is important to determine consumption trends since the processing and packaging of vegetables and fruits involves metals, paper, plastics, etc., and thus affects the demand for these other resources. It is difficult to isolate any factors which would make for either a substantially increased or decreased consumption per capita of vegetables and fruits. Expected, however, is a further decline in the consumption of potatoes, offset by increases in consumption of other vegetables such as tomatoes and the leafy green vegetables, accompanied by an increase in the per capita consumption of citrus fruit, hand in hand with a decline of other fruits. The increase in

per capita consumption of fruits as a whole over the next
forty years probably will not exceed 10 per cent.

New Sources of Food

Somewhere over the rainbow lie new sources of food:
processed fish flour, algae, synthetic carbohydrates or proteins
compounded with artificial textures and made palatable with
any of a vast assortment of artificial flavors. Private industry
and governments have been at work trying to expand the
conventional resource basis of our food supply. The driving
force, however, has not been concern over limitations of
cropland, at least not in this country, nor excessive food cost;
rather, it has been the drive to explore new frontiers of science. Technological progress in food production is more likely
to seek increases in yields and efficiency in traditional ways
of supplying food, rather than breakthroughs into utterly new
provinces of food production. This assumption may prove
wrong long before the end of the century—and it does not
hold equally true for the less-developed countries of the
world—but at this particular time it does not seem practical
to treat new sources of food as statistically significant.

FIBERS: NATURAL vs. MAN-MADE

Not very far back in history, man-made fibers supplied
only a minute quantity of the total fiber market. Even twenty-
five years ago, only 12 per cent of the fiber market was supplied by man-made fibers. Today it is more like 40 per cent,
and the percentage is rising. New fibers are finding increasing
use not only as the exclusive content of fabrics, but in combination with natural fibers and with each other.

There are probably very few uses in which, cost considerations apart, man-made fibers could not replace natural. What
began years ago with the replacement of silk stockings by
nylon has now reached the point where the natural fur coat

can be replaced by a synthetic one that is similar in looks and comfort, if not in prestige. Fiberglass is now used for draperies and curtains, and felted "paper" fabrics for disposable garments in industrial plants and laboratories.

Clothing Trends

As has been seen, there are fairly narrow limits to up or down movements in the consumption of foods and even for specific food items. But nobody has yet figured out, or has been willing to say, what the "normal" wardrobe of a man or woman or child in this country should be. The "3,200 calories or so" has no equivalent in a standard yardage or poundage of textiles.

There are two strong but conflicting trends in consumption of clothing: on the one hand, there are more people every year with more money to spend; on the other, outlays for clothing have been taking a progressively smaller share of the family budget. The net result has been a moderate increase in aggregate spending for clothing which has, however, lagged behind the rise in population and total buying power.

Factors in this lag include: new products with better wearing quality or which are readily washable and dryable, obviating the necessity for a larger wardrobe; air conditioning in summer and heating in winter, causing a blurring of the line, once very strict, between summer clothing and winter clothing; acceptability of casual clothing; a tendency for a higher proportion of the labor force to spend its working day indoors; rapid transit, reducing the time spent outdoors; migration to warmer climates.

To state the decline in money terms: of every dollar of additional income, a smaller share than in the past is going for clothing. This is true of both fiber and apparel consumption. In the last 15 years, fiber consumption for apparel has been on a plateau of 19 to 20 pounds per year per person. This is by no means a small quantity—it is twice the amount that the average Western European consumes, and at least four times that of a resident of a country like India.

Forty years ago, the average man's suit appears to have been made of fabric weighing as much as 20 ounces per linear yard. By 1952, the clothing trade regarded "regular-weight worsteds" as meaning materials weighing 12 to 13 ounces per linear yard; by 1958 the term was taken to mean no more than 11 to 12 ounces. Style changes have also moved in the direction of less fabric per garment: the vest as a regular component of a man's business suit has gone; so have many articles of clothing once standard equipment in a woman's wardrobe and those that have remained tend to be short and slim. The composition of the United States population in the last few decades has been increasingly weighted with young children and older adults, both of whom require less fabric than young adults. Synthetic fibers, pound for pound, usually provide more fabric than their natural counterparts; yard for yard they last longer and thus enable consumers to maintain larger wardrobes without correspondingly larger current purchases.

Some factors that exerted downward pressures in the recent past no longer operate, such as high clothing purchases after World War II and the Korean conflict and the perhaps consequent depression of expenditures for clothing in the 1950's as a whole. The trend to lighter-weight garments, while probably continuing, is unlikely to proceed at the same rate as in the past. The high rate of family formation, with new families giving high priority to purchases other than clothing, may, however, be expected to continue for some time. This trend will be reinforced by the suburban living which a large proportion of these young households has adopted, as it encourages casual clothing. Radical innovations—such as the appearance of extremely cheap, disposable, paper-like garments—would, of course, play havoc with these projections. So could a more than temporary return to longer dresses, which is not too likely in view of prospective employment patterns for women.

Of the total fiber consumption expressed in cotton-equivalent pounds (that is, all fabrics or fibers translated to what they would be if made of cotton), the apparel segment accounts for about half. This proportion is expected to remain constant in the future. The other half consists, in about equal amounts, of household and industrial textiles.

Home Use

Household textiles include carpets and rugs, linens (sheets, pillowcases, towels, now made primarily of cotton), upholstery materials, curtains, and drapes. Within this large variety, linens are far and away the most important item. This fact lends a basic stability to household textile requirements, since per capita demand for linens can be expected to change less than that for clothing, and displacement of cotton by lighter weight fabrics on a large scale is not at present on the horizon. The demand for household textiles, especially those other than linens, responds to rising incomes, and has been given further impetus by the high rate of establishment of new and larger households.

Cotton has retained a firm hold on this segment of textiles. Important gains have been made by rayon and other synthetics (blankets, tablecloths, drapes, rugs), but the natural fibers have managed to maintain a substantial importance. Assumed for the future is continuation of an upward trend in per capita consumption for the entire household group, with an increasing rate of substitution of synthetic for natural fibers. As a result, household use should slightly strengthen its relative importance as a textile market.

Industry Use

Perhaps one-fourth of the so-called industrial category of fiber use goes into automobile tires; a large amount goes into other parts of automobiles; an additional although declining amount finds its way into packaging. Heavy inroads have been made into industrial use of natural fibers, partly by synthetic fibers, but partly by entirely different materials. The automobile industry has found increasing ways to substitute plastic for fibers. Paper has driven cotton out of the packaging field for household items like salt, sugar, and flour, and as bagging for such materials as cement and feed. Expressed in cotton-equivalent pounds, the share of synthetics went from 3 per cent of industrial use in 1937 to 34 per cent in 1949, and currently stands at about 65 per cent. Two past trends are expected to continue: a declining use of fibers per unit of industrial output, which will cause a steady decline in the relative importance of this segment; and an increase in the use of synthetics.

Shares Among the Fibers

On the above assumptions, the greatest rate of growth in fiber consumption will be in household use, which will rise almost 3½ times between 1960 and the end of the century. Industrial use will only double during the same time; apparel use will increase somewhat less than 3 times. Within the aggregates, the share of cotton, which dropped from about 65 per cent in 1950 to only 56 per cent in 1960, will drop farther but less rapidly; by the end of the century it will have declined to about 44 per cent. Natural wool, which now accounts for only 5 per cent of the market, is expected to slide to less than 2 per cent of the total fiber market by 2000. The man-made fibers, today accounting for 40 per cent of the fiber market, by the end of the century should furnish as much as 54 per cent. On any assumption, it is unlikely that the share of man-made fibers will be lower than 50 or higher than 60 per cent of total fiber consumption by the end of the century. Figure 10 shows the outlook for major uses and principal kinds of fiber.

The so-called noncellulosic fibers—synthetic fibers other than rayon and acetate—have had a spectacular rise, and

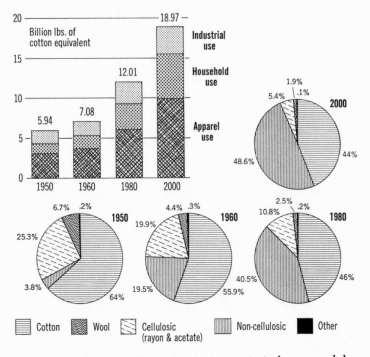

Figure 10. Trends in fiber consumption: principal uses, and how natural and man-made types share the total market.

today account for half of all man-made fibers, compared to only 13 per cent 10 years ago. They will probably eventually account for the bulk of the synthetic fiber market—by the end of the century 90 per cent of the synthetic market is projected as belonging to the noncellulosic fibers.

In terms of actual weight rather than the common denominator of cotton-equivalent weight, total consumption of cotton fibers is now more than twice that of the man-made fibers including rayon and acetate, and it will still account for more poundage at the end of the century because of its higher weight per unit. Cotton fiber consumption should increase from 4 billion pounds in 1960 to a little more than 8 billion pounds in the year 2000. In contrast, the synthetics should increase from 1.8 billion pounds in 1960 to about 5.8 billion pounds in 2000—that is, more than three times. For the synthetics other than rayon or acetate, the projected rise is even more dramatic: from 800 million pounds in 1960 to over 5 billion pounds in 2000.

The major implication for natural resources is the transition from a material like cotton that is intimately tied to soil and climate to substances that are created by chemical synthesis, using predominantly oil and natural gas as starting materials today, but potentially also producible from coal. Rayon and acetate, derived from forest resources, will constitute a rapidly diminishing share of the synthetics market. Continuing substitution in the field of fibers thus involves the ultimate transition from a potentially scarce resource—cotton land—to one that in this country at least may be considered as inexhaustible for a long time to come—hydrocarbons.

THE MANY FACETS OF CONSTRUCTION

Timber, stone, and clay have since time immemorial been the resources from which shelter has been fashioned. But glass, a growing variety of metals, and most recently plastics and other synthetic materials have gradually entered the field of construction materials.

Residential housing is only a portion of total construction. In value—the only common unit of measurement—new housing accounts for one-third. The other components of construction represent a large variety of activities, both public and private, the most important of which are highways, public utilities, and stores and offices. Maintenance and repair by itself is almost as large as new residential construction. Figure 11 shows the current composition of the construction total.

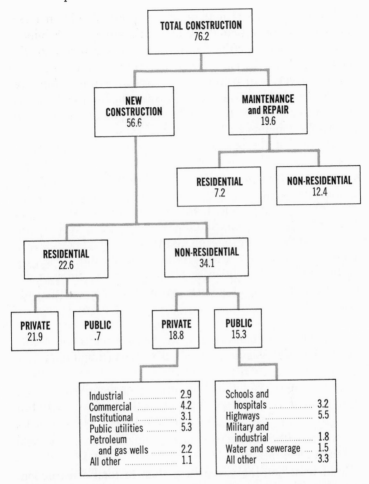

Figure 11. Principal categories of construction in 1960, in billions of 1960 dollars.

Residential Housing

Needed between now and 1980 are some 20 million additional dwellings, or 1 million per year on the average. Because of the growing rate of household formation, the annual average will increase to about 1.2 million new dwellings per year to provide some 50 million units in the period between 1960 and 2000.

These levels, which would accommodate the growing number of households, are not greatly different from those of the last ten years or so. But the projection provides for a rate of construction about 10 per cent higher, since there is reason to believe that the so-called vacancy rate—that is, the ratio between the units not occupied and the total number—will increase slightly from here on. This will be largely the result of the increasing number of "two-house families."

Much more important than any assumptions with regard to vacancy rates are assumptions with regard to replacement demand—that is, the rate of disappearance both of existing houses and of those yet to be built. Housing units disappear as the result of demolition or abandonment, or through disaster by fire, flood, or windstorm. Some are converted into rooming houses, stores, or offices. Others are lost by merger with other units—as when two apartments are turned into one, or when basement apartments become recreation rooms. Demolition and abandonment do not always result from age. Many dwellings are demolished while still serviceable to make room for highways, office buildings, apartment houses, and other structures. Dwellings may be abandoned as a result of migration, and allowed to deteriorate to a point where they are lost to the housing supply.

These losses are to some degree balanced by gains not involving new construction. Units are not only merged—they can also be subdivided. Stores, garages, barns, and other buildings, or parts of them, are converted to residential use. Rooming houses have individual cooking facilities added and become tenements.

Replacement measurement statistics are unsatisfactory, sometimes even misleading. But it appears that during two periods in the last thirty years or so, little attention was given to replacement: the first during the depression decade of the 1930's, the second during the war years of the 1940's.

In 1940, the age of the average house was 30 years. By 1950 it had increased to 35 years, and it is still at about that figure since new construction after 1950 has just about kept up with current aging. Future rates of replacement are assumed to be such as to bring the average age down to about 30 years by 1970 and 25 years by the end of the century. This projection supposes that there will not be much change over the next several decades in the typical kinds of houses we live in—at least not in their durability; it also supposes that mortgage credit and other background conditions will permit the continuous elimination of older units at the more rapid rates characteristic of the late 1950's. Some perspective is lent these figures by the National Housing Inventory, taken in 1956 by the U.S. Bureau of the Census, which classified nearly a million units as "dilapidated" and found 8½ million lacking a private toilet, a bath, or hot running water.

In order to reduce the average age of houses to 30 years by 1970, it will be necessary to replace about 10½ million units during the decade ending in that year. In subsequent decades this replacement quota would grow. By the last decade of the century, 16½ million units would have to be built to replace old houses. Figure 12 shows how replacements have compared with net additions in the past and what the prospects are between now and the end of the century.

These expectations may be somewhat optimistic. But the combination of a large stock of aged housing and the prospect of continuously growing income in a society that is beginning to slow down its expenditures for food and clothing may prove to be a substantial stimulus.

There are those who speak of the advent of "annual model" houses, like new-model automobiles. One need by no means go that far. While housing in the past has not been given to revolutions, it is conceivable that its pace could be quickened, assisted perhaps by a far-reaching urban renewal program and

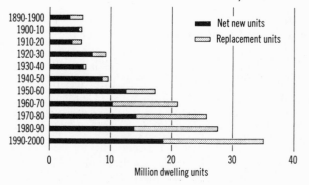

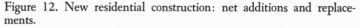

Figure 12. New residential construction: net additions and replacements.

by significant introduction of new methods and materials, so that a rate of replacement of mature stock would be attained that would substantially exceed even the projections here made.

The net outcome of these assumptions is 2.4 million new housing starts per year by 1970, rising to 4.2 million annual housing starts by the end of the century. These projections include farm housing starts, and are adjusted for other omissions in the official series, which tends to underestimate the number of total housing starts. (To be comparable with government statistics on new nonfarm housing starts, our projections would have to be reduced to 2.0 million and 3.6 million respectively.)

In terms of expenditure, residential new construction would rise from not quite $23 billion in 1960 to not quite $55 billion in 1980, or about 2½ times. It would rise about 2⅓ times further between 1980 and 2000. For purposes of comparison, the projected increase in spending for new dwellings amounts to only 4½ per cent per year between 1960 and 1980, and a slightly lower percentage between 1980 and 2000—as compared with over 6 per cent per year between 1946 and 1960.

Nonresidential Construction

Nonresidential construction accounts for nearly two-thirds of total construction. No single sector dominates. Highway construction, amounting to about $5½ billion in 1960 is among the larger categories. Public utilities construction is of about the same magnitude. Commercial facilities absorbed about $4¼ billion in 1960, while construction of schools, hospitals, and private institutional construction amounted to $3¼ billion each. A little more than half of all nonresidential construction is now financed privately, and a little less than half publicly. The distinction merits attention, since the latter is far more subject to sudden spurts or delays as a result of changes in public policy.

Each of the components of nonresidential construction can be found to be logically related to either an economic or social factor that is more easily projected. This opens a way to throw light on future construction.

Thus private industrial construction, which comprises the building of factories and other processing facilities, is related to investment in manufacturing; construction of institutional and miscellaneous buildings to population growth; utility construction to utility gas and power sales; highway construction to highway miles traveled by automobiles and trucks— qualified by the assumption that highway construction will rise faster than miles traveled. (See Figure 13.)

An important item in the construction field is maintenance and repair. As one assumes a rising rate of replacement one must, to be consistent, reduce the amount of funds spent on maintenance and repair, which is an alternative to replacement (and which, incidentally, serves as a corrective in case one has overestimated the number of replacement units). Hence, in the projections, the outlays for maintenance and repair of dwellings have been methodically reduced relative to new construction. At present $1.00 is spent in keeping

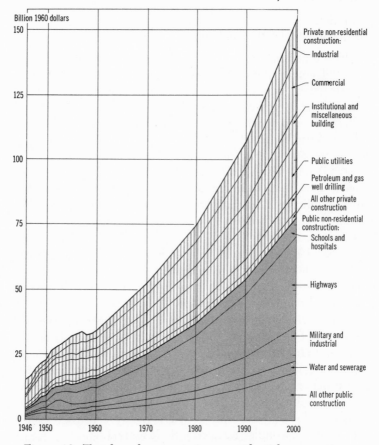

Figure 13. Trends and prospects in nonresidential construction.

existing houses in good repair for every $3.00 spent on new residential construction. Forty years from now, the ratio is likely to be 1:8.

Construction Materials

To arrive at the amounts of materials that are required in construction, it is necessary, first, to relate the expenditures just described to physical consumption data for major construction materials (steel, lumber, cement, etc.); second, to form a judgment as to whether the materials used today will continue to be utilized in the future in more or less the same proportions. Construction in this sense includes not merely the structural members of a house, bridge, or steel mill, but the very large amount of auxiliary equipment required, whether functional or decorative.

In home building, one of the major structural developments since World War II has been a shift from the wooden frame house to masonry structures and, to a limited extent, to metallic frames and structural panels. Frame houses have increasingly been sheathed with insulation board and plywood instead of wood boards. In some areas of the country there has been a trend toward brick veneer and brick-wood combination facing. There have also appeared some all-aluminum and all-plastic houses, but these are still essentially experimental. The prefabricated house industry is another instance of a new departure, but fewer than 100,000 units a year are being shipped currently.

New construction methods have advanced farther in apartment and office buildings and in industrial plants and the like than in home building. Instances are the frequent use of curtain walls of steel, aluminum, or plastic panels; on-the-site precasting of concrete; use of prefabricated sandwich panels of metal, plastic, asbestos board, wood composition board, plywood, asbestos cement, and light-weight concrete. New applications of conventional materials accompany uses of new materials: plastic foam for core material in sandwich panels; flooring of a variety of materials such as plastic, cork or rubber tiles, plywood, poured concrete or precast gypsum or concrete slabs, and asphalt. An outstanding development in ceiling and interior wall construction in homes, as well as other buildings, is the gradual abandonment of plaster in favor of so-called "dry wall" construction mostly of gypsum board.

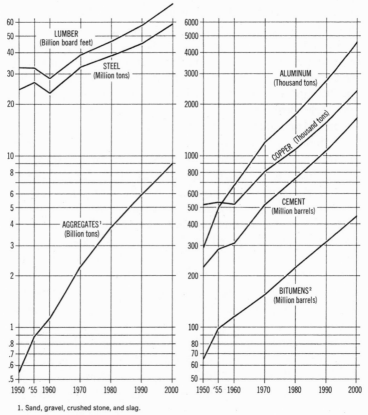

1. Sand, gravel, crushed stone, and slag.

2. Highway paving accounts for 80-90% of the total; the remainder is used principally for roofing.

Figure 14. Changing rates of use of principal construction materials.

Besides their use in floor and wall tiles and for reinforced fiberglass paneling in roofing, plastics are of potential importance in construction where color and translucence are valued. Plastics will probably be used increasingly as the principal core materials and as an important surface material for sandwich panels; as a substitute for wood in concrete forms; as floor surfacing; and as surfacing material for blocks and tiles made of other substances. Plastic glues, some of which have proven stronger than rivets in joining metal sheets to each other, are used in cabinetwork and in making plywood. Both copper and steel are likely to see their plastic competitor become an acceptable and even preferable substitute for pipes and fittings, once building codes permit and building contractors adopt such use.

The large-scale adoption of plastics and other synthetics for building depends ultimately not only on the nature of the new varieties and their relative prices, but on such unpredictable but crucial factors as building codes and architectural styles. Further technological breakthroughs such as imparting strength through irradiation might well qualify plastics as structural materials, too. At the moment, however, no quantitative projection of the use of plastics in building can be reasonably made. Plastics, in more general categories, are discussed later on, in connection with the future use of petrochemicals. The future of structural materials such as glass and gypsum is not analyzed either, largely because these materials do not imply national problems. Figure 14 shows the quantities now consumed and projections for important construction materials: lumber, steel, cement, aggregates, bitumens, aluminum, and copper.

THE NEEDS OF TRANSPORTATION

One out of every five units of energy consumed in the United States goes towards moving people or materials. One-fifth of the final value of all the end products and services of the U.S. economy is accounted for by transportation expenditure. Transport ranks high as a consumer of metal, be it in the production of motor vehicles, railroad cars, airplanes, or ships. The aluminum industry has grown with the spread of the airplane, and truck and trailer bodies use a significant amount of aluminum. Two of today's large outlets for lead are storage batteries and gasoline to which lead is added.

Automobile tires are the major consumer of rubber, natural and synthetic.

Passenger Transportation

The automotive age is not much more than fifty years old—in 1914 only 1.6 million cars were registered in the United States. By 1960, this country had almost 60 million automobiles—a doubling of automobile registrations since the end of World War II.

This startling, and unforeseen, advance is not a good reason to expect a similar rate of growth in the next four decades. While it is obvious that we have not reached the growth limit predicted more than once in the past, saturation is substantially closer today than even ten years ago. We now have one car for every two adults. By the time we have one for every adult, further increases may be more difficult to achieve. While production of automobiles will continue with the growth of population and with continuous replacement of obsolete cars, the increase in the ratio between cars and adults can be expected to slow down.

What are the determinants of automobile ownership? Income, perhaps the most important, is only one of many. For example, westerners own more cars per family than easterners, and population is generally moving West. Suburban families own more cars than do city families. Differentiation among different types of automobiles—for shopping, for sport, for vacation driving, etc.—is another factor increasing the number of automobiles per adult.

Looking ahead forty years, there is the possibility of an "auto-plane" coming into existence and use. One should perhaps be talking not of the automobile as it is today, but of the "owner-operated vehicle" whether it moves on the ground on conventional wheels, on an air cushion, or in the air.

In continuation of a rising trend that reduced the number of adults (aged 20 or over) per car from 2.8 in 1950 to 1.9 in 1960, one owner-operated vehicle is projected for every

1.3 adults by 1980, and perhaps more than one for every adult by the end of the century. While this would signify a substantial slowing down of the past rate, the momentum of population growth would raise the total vehicles operated by their owners from 59 million in 1960 to 120 million in 1980, and to over 240 million in the year 2000. In other words, by the end of the century there would be four vehicles for every one operating today.

Such a development is scarcely compatible with our current streets, highways, and parking facilities. The auxiliary facilities to permit such expansion of vehicles, whether solely land-borne or land-air borne, would have to be adjusted to permit such an increase. Since traffic planning usually calls for compromises between many interested groups, and typically is a long-range effort, the outlook here projected for passenger vehicles, while it may appear fanciful at first glance, may be useful for adjusting one's sights in sufficient time. Furthermore, in putting forward such speculations, one must be mindful that in the past the saturation levels of automobile ownerships were assumed to be far lower than those which subsequently came to pass. A consequence has been the rush-hour traffic on weekdays, and the bumper-to-bumper freeway, beltway, parkway or expressway traffic near metropolitan centers on weekends. Automobile drivers have thus far been willing to pay this price in exchange for auto ownership—their forbearance may have a breaking point.

Besides population growth and spread of ownership, the replacement of worn-out vehicles is an important determinant of automobile production—with which we are concerned in order to estimate material consumption, other than fuel. The rate of replacement can be roughly approximated on the basis of an average lifetime of about eleven years. Inclusive of replacement demand, total domestic purchases of automobiles should increase from the 7 million in 1960 to twice that number in 1980, and twice that number again in 2000. (See Figure 15.)

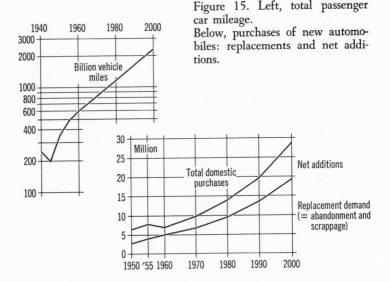

Figure 15. Left, total passenger car mileage.
Below, purchases of new automobiles: replacements and net additions.

Neither in fuel consumption, nor in mileage traveled nor in call on construction materials do other forms of passenger transportation begin to approach automobiles. The annual mileage traveled by passenger automobiles in this country is somewhere around 10,000 miles per car. Even if no passenger car ever carried more than one person—obviously a radical understatement—this would amount to over 3,000 miles per year per person (59 million cars × 10,000 passenger miles ÷ 180 million people). Comparable rates in 1960 were 96 miles per capita for rail transport, 113 miles for bus transport, and 192 miles for air transport—mere fractions of what automobiles carry.

Comparisons in terms of fuel requirements are equally striking. Automobiles consumed about 40 billion gallons of fuel in 1960, buses 1 billion. Railroads consumed in the neighborhood of 4 billion gallons, or one-tenth the amount consumed by automobiles, and airplanes about 2 billion.

Figure 16 shows the amounts of liquid fuel used by the various forms of transportation in 1960 and projections for 1980 and 2000.

The story is similar concerning the materials from which transportation carriers are built. Again automobiles predominate. Trucks and trailers are also important consumers. Railroads, which are second to motor vehicles, are responsible for 3 to 5 per cent of steel consumption, and for about 5 per cent of lumber consumption. Airplanes are of some, but minor, importance in the aluminum consumption picture.

Many interesting aspects of public passenger transportation relate to matters other than their call on resources: competition between short-haul railways and buses, the future role of short- and medium-haul air traffic, the dependence of the inner cities upon adequate transportation facilities, etc. In the context of this study we have had to gloss over most of these problems, given the all-pervasive importance of the automobile as a consumer of both fuel and structural material.

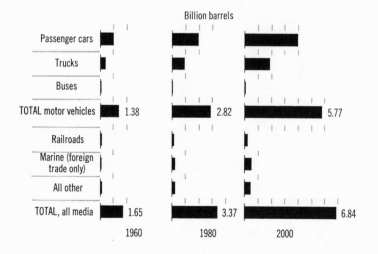

Figure 16. Use of liquid fuel in different kinds of transportation.

Freight Transportation

In moving goods, the main problem is not the projection of the total volume of traffic, as this will probably continue to grow with almost clocklike precision in line with the nation's output of goods. What is difficult is to determine how this traffic will be divided among the different modes of transportation: rail, truck, pipeline, air, and waterways.

In the past, rail traffic has progressively lost out to trucks and pipelines, in large part as the consequence of the declining role of coal in the economy. While coal moves principally by rail, its competitors—oil and gas—move in pipelines, tankers, and barges, and for shorter hauls in trucks. To the extent that these fuel substitutions are coming to an end, the effect on the different transportation media will decline, and the long downward trend in rail traffic can be expected to flatten out.

A challenge to a renewed upswing of railroad freight traffic could develop from perfection of competitive pipeline movements of solids. At this moment it is particularly hard to appraise the prospects of success. In the first place, the railways have begun to offer improved and cheaper freight service. This led to the shutdown in 1963 of the only operating coal pipeline, though, in this instance, the feasibility of the pipeline principle seems to have been fully vindicated since it took a cut of nearly 50 per cent in the rail rate to render the pipeline nonoperative. Rail competition is also causing a slowdown in planning for at least two new coal pipelines that are to carry large tonnages to the Eastern seaboard. Pipeline construction will require public action for acquisition of right-of-way, with the prospect of long legislative battles involving rail, coal, and pipeline interests.

Long-distance, high-voltage transmission of coal-generated electricity is coming of age, threatening railroad expansion, and its perfection could open up distant hydroelectric potential, in competition with thermal power development.

An element that might boost railroad traffic would be further development of containers that can be easily transferred from truck to rail and from rail to truck, thus better co-ordinating these two main land-based modes of long-distance transport. Offsetting this is the prospect of multi-trailer trucks carrying goods over long distances, just as water transport has received an enormous impetus from the development of barge-trains that combine as many as thirty individual barges into one unit.

Figure 17 shows the most probable outcome of these divergent trends: a gradual halting in the decline of the railroads' share, matched by an increase and subsequent stabilization in the share of trucking, unchanged relative participation of inland waterways, and a slight rise in the relative share of pipelines (oil pipelines only, since the freight statistics do not

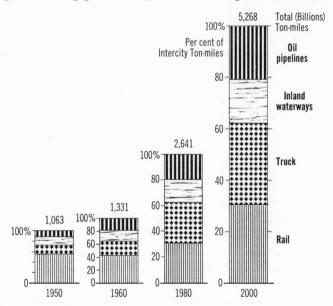

Figure 17. Shares of freight transportation among principal kinds of carrier and rise in total ton-mileage.

include gas transportation). The role of air transport, while increasing, will still be so small even at the end of the century that it can be neglected. It would take a major breakthrough —not now on the horizon—to bring air freight to such prominence as to make it worth while to speculate concerning its share in total transportation of goods, either in terms of fuel consumption or of materials needed for construction of air carriers.

Consumption of Materials by Transportation

The consequences of error in attempting to foresee the sharing of traffic between different means of transportation are mitigated by two facts: (1) all transportation uses essentially one type of fuel, petroleum, directly or via electricity (as in diesel locomotives), and (2) metals constitute the main material from which carriers are made. In the latter case, some differences could be significant. For example, the more the truck-manufacturing industry shifts from steel to aluminum, the more important is the division of traffic between rail and trucks. Yet there remains sufficient similarity in materials consumption to render less damaging any errors made in the projected allocation of freight volume.

Material consumption by transportation is very large: about 25 per cent of all steel consumed, about 10 per cent of all copper, 20 per cent of all aluminum and zinc, and 5 per cent of all glass. Automotive batteries account for about one-fourth of all lead consumed, and rubber tires for almost 7 out of every 10 pounds of rubber used in this country.

Motor vehicles, including trucks and buses, are the largest consumers. Vehicles built in 1960 contained around 10 million tons of steel, 2½ million tons of cast iron, nearly 250,000 tons of aluminum, over 300,000 tons of lead, nearly 200,000 tons of zinc, and over 150,000 tons of copper. In addition, 1¼ million tons of rubber, 500,000 tons of glass, 200,000 bales of cotton, and 70,000 tons of plastic are being consumed annually by motor vehicles. With such large amounts being used, even moderate changes in the design of motor vehicles can make a substantial difference in the future demand for different materials.

The average automobile produced in 1960 weighed something like 3,500 pounds, of which 2,400 pounds was steel, 600 cast iron, 60 aluminum, and the remainder other materials. While one may reasonably expect the average size of cars not to change much in the future, their future average weight is much more uncertain. Substitution of aluminum for iron and steel makes vehicles lighter, hence capable of being propelled by smaller power plants; this, in turn, means they need less structural strength, so that they can become lighter still.

Displacement of iron and steel by aluminum reached significant proportions with the 1961 models, of which some ten were equipped with aluminum engine blocks. Other applications have been transmission housing, piston heads, connecting rods, brake parts, and body trim. Yet aluminum still accounts for less than 2 per cent of average car weight, and in some instances the transition to an aluminum engine has been halted or reversed. In some cars made in Europe, on the other hand, substitution of aluminum has gone a long way. Designers estimate that eventually it would be advantageous to build a car with as much as 350 to 400 pounds of aluminum, compared to the current average American car content of only about 60 or 65 pounds. The relative economy achieved by using aluminum rather than steel, depending on price developments, will ultimately decide this competitive struggle. But recent history makes it reasonable to provide a larger role for aluminum in the future.

Compared with automobile use, the total quantities of aluminum consumed in the manufacture of trucks and trailers are small, but the inroads of aluminum upon steel and cast iron have been great. In the construction of trailer van bodies in particular, aluminum is now the primary material, and an increasing proportion of all trailers are vans.

Aluminum is also beginning to encroach upon steel in the manufacture of pipe for pipelines—a development that may become a major factor in the future. For the small-diameter pipes, aluminum has already established itself as a potential competitor. Steel has countered this offensive by making pipes with thinner walls without sacrificing strength. With aluminum pipe challenging steel even as drill pipe, it is certainly time to take notice.

Lead, zinc, and copper are the other principal metals used in motor vehicles. Since batteries do not last nearly so long as automobiles, the use of lead is largely determined by the replacement market. Unless the traditional storage type battery using lead plates is replaced by an essentially different one such as the special-purpose nickel or cadmium battery used largely by the military, it is unlikely that the life expectation of automotive batteries will change. The trend to larger batteries, from the 6-volt to the 12-volt, does not greatly upset the projections, as the larger size uses only about 10 per cent more lead. With extra equipment added to automobiles, such as air conditioning and power accessories, it is quite possible that batteries will get larger still. These conflicting tendencies, coupled with uncertainty regarding the future total automobile population and the annual production, make estimating difficult. It seems clear, however, that, barring unforeseen new applications, the rate of growth of lead cannot be very large.

For copper and zinc, motor vehicles are not so important a market as for lead. Uncertainty as to the future role of zinc derives mainly from the competitive attack of aluminum and plastics. A big question mark in the future use of copper is the role of radiators, as air-cooled aluminum engines would certainly greatly curtail their use. On the other hand, the use of copper in wiring would increase with the addition of accessory equipment powered by electricity. Projections of metal use in motor vehicles are shown in Figure 18.

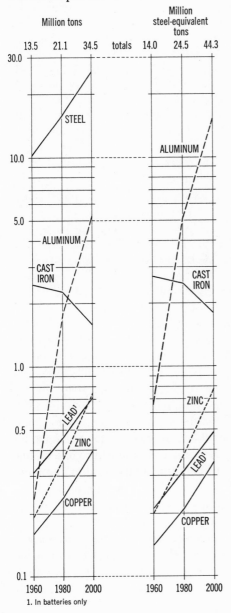

Figure 18. How the use of metals in motor vehicles may develop.

New Modes of Transport

There is hardly any imaginable type of vehicle of which a prototype has not been constructed. Some of these are the jet-propelled hedge-hopping vehicle, the moving sidewalk, the monorail, the vertical take-off and landing plane, the giant petroleum-filled rubber or plastic bag towed by a ship, the hydrofoil ship moving at 60 miles an hour or more above the water, the rapid transit bus moving both on rails and on pavements, the remote-controlled automobile traveling on superspeed tracks, the pipeline carrying grain or other bulky materials, and, of course, rocket propulsion for long-distance movement of either people or goods.

No matter how a vehicle is driven, it will still have to be built of some kind of structural materials, and for the moment metals remain the most likely candidate. With small exceptions, most vehicles will still have to be propelled by a combustible fuel, either directly or by way of electricity. In the field of nuclear propulsion only the ship is a reality. Neither nuclear plane nor locomotive seems near, and the nuclear automotive battery is not even standing in the wings. To be sure, efficiencies in converting energy to movement are likely to change, perhaps substantially. But when we consider the length of time—at least two decades—that the gas turbine has been on the horizon as an automotive engine, it is not likely that far more radical departures from conventional engines will have much effect in the next two decades, perhaps not even in the next four. Our projections, though conservative, may therefore turn out to be surprisingly close to the mark.

DURABLE GOODS

It is customary these days to stress the importance of services in the modern economy. This is due partly to the fact that in our national economic accounts one of the largest entries in the service category is housing, measured by the imputed value of its use. It appears as a service just as does a doctor's call or the cashing of a check. But even with this generous definition of services, those tangible items called goods still constitute half of the national output, and are likely to decline in importance only moderately in the coming decades.

Many of these goods are easily categorized and have been discussed. Food, clothing, shelter, and fuel are the most prominent among them. Most other things can conveniently be summed up as "durables." Production of durables is a large item in the economy: it amounted to almost 20 per cent of the gross national product in 1960. Not quite one-third consisted of transportation equipment, discussed previously, and another 15 per cent or so of military hardware. This leaves a miscellaneous group ranging from industrial machinery, furniture, and fixtures to household appliances and electrical equipment, tools and instruments, sporting goods, and tableware and utensils. This group is traditionally divided into consumer and producer durables, each representing about 50 per cent of this mixed bag of products.

The durability of durables should not be taken too literally: an article of clothing, such as a pair of shoes, may outlast an educational toy or a garden rake—yet the latter two fall statistically under the heading "consumer durables." The distinction makes more sense in the case of so-called "producer durables," which include such things as transportation equipment, electrical and industrial machinery, office equipment, agricultural machinery such as tractors, and the like.

Most durables are also known as "hard goods," a reminder of the fact that, with exceptions such as rubber tires and tubes and household articles such as draperies, most are rigid or semirigid and made of metal, wood, or, more recently, plastic.

Consumer Durables

Today, 98 per cent of all households in the United States have refrigerators, 94 per cent radios, and 95 per cent washing machines. Many households have more than one of each. In view of this, where will future production find a market?

In the first place, appliances are replaced every so often, frequently before they wear out, because something new and better has come on the market. Thus the 90 per cent of all households now content with black-and-white television may someday find they cannot get along without color. Many now owning refrigerators with an 11 cubic-foot capacity, shelving in the door, a large freezing compartment and automatic defrosting were satisfied, not so long ago, with a model with only 7 cubic-foot capacity, no freezer and no defroster.

Other appliances are nowhere near market saturation. For example, only 7 per cent of all households own dishwashers, only 10 per cent have food waste disposers, and only 20 per cent clothes dryers. A widely acceptable automatic ironer is still to reach the market. Other appliances may not even be on the drawing board.

As mentioned, one appliance per household by no means constitutes saturation. Two or three radios, two vacuum cleaners, two electric irons—one for traveling, one for home use—are no longer marks of luxurious living. Two television sets, particularly in families with young children, are no more extraordinary than several photographic cameras in the same family. A kitchen where precooked dishes can be transferred to an automatic warming oven and carted to the family dining table by pushing buttons cannot, given a forty-year perspective, be ruled out.

There is no visible end to the stream of appliances which will be invented, perfected, desired, and purchased. Generally increasing incomes are expanding both the range of felt needs and the means of satisfying them. Many things that are known only to the rich of one generation are regarded as necessities by the next. Not all of these things fall within the traditional category of durables, but most of them do.

Rapid changes in style are another factor tending to increase purchases and production of consumer durables. Furniture is discarded to make room for what has been seen and liked in the latest home furnishing magazine. Such consumer behavior rests on a trend of rising income, that makes refurnishing a house less of a problem. Since on the average, as has been seen, expenditures for food and clothing no longer take such a high percentage of the family budget, more money can be spent on other items.

When projections of expenditures on consumer durables other than autos and automobile accessories are added together, they are seen to be growing somewhat faster than the gross national product. Consumer durable expenditures in the year 2000 are estimated at more than five times the 1960 level, whereas gross national product during the same period grows only four times. The two categories growing faster than any of the others are household appliances and a mixed category called books, toys, and sports equipment which to a large extent reflects an increase in leisure time. Table 1 shows projections of annual per capita expenditures for various types of consumer durables.

Table 1. Annual Per Capita Expenditures for Consumer Durables
(1960 dollars)

Consumer durables	1960	1980	2000
Autos and accessories	104	159	231
Household appliances	46	95	171
Furniture and furnishings	47	73	108
Books, toys, and sports equipment	19	38	72
Tableware and utensils	12	16	24
Jewelry and watches	12	19	28
Medical appliances, eyeglasses, etc.	7	11	16
Total	247	411	650

Producer Durables

Projected purchases of producer durables—the machines and tools needed to produce goods and perform services—

yield a rate of growth similar to that of consumer durables. Both are likely to quintuple over the next forty years.

That there is a close relationship between the amount of capital invested in plant and equipment and the magnitude of the resulting output is obvious, but to identify any changes in this relationship in the past and discover their causes is not only statistically difficult but embroiled in a continuing controversy dealing with the capital/output ratio in our economy, and with economic growth in general. Rather than trying to reason from this or that theory for the economy as a whole we have here preferred to build up the total picture from its components. This has meant (1) investigating the relationship between annual output and investment in plant and equipment in a half dozen or so major industrial and service categories; (2) projecting that relationship into the future; (3) determining the kinds and volume of equipment —as opposed to other investment—that have been associated with each large economic segment, such as electrical machinery, service machinery, etc.; and (4) projecting into the future this second relationship. Table 2 shows the end result: the projected purchases of producer durables, by type of equipment. When the projections are aggregated we have a measure, always in dollars, of total producer durable purchases per year. From these, in turn, one can reason as to material requirements.

One need hardly stress that both steps, the reasoning from size of output to magnitude of required investment, and the reasoning from size of investment to types of equipment, are hazardous. New processes may raise or lower the amount of capital needed per unit of output in any or all pursuits. Machinery may be made to last longer, or it may be utilized at higher rates of capacity. Types of equipment may change, and so forth. Nonetheless, only in the presence of strong indications that these relationships were changing has any deviation from past experience been postulated.

Table 2. Trends in Producer Durable Purchases

(Billion 1960 dollars)

Producer durables	1950	1960	1980	2000
Transportation equipment. (incl. passenger cars)	8.7	7.4	17.2	34.8
Electrical machinery	2.5	3.4	7.2	14.9
Industrial machinery, not electric	5.3	5.1	11.6	22.3
Furniture and fixtures	1.4	2.1	4.3	8.6
Service-industry machinery	1.2	1.8	3.3	8.3
Other nonagricultural equipment	4.1	6.2	13.6	29.5
Agricultural machinery	2.6	1.5	2.7	3.6
Balance to reconcile sum of items with independently estimated total below	—	—	7.0	23.2
Total	25.8	27.5	66.9	145.2

Materials for Durables

For a long time, both producer and consumer durables have been made largely of metals and wood. To this, plastics have recently been added. On the basis of tonnage involved, metals are still the chief ingredient. Wood, used principally in furniture, is declining, while plastics are growing. But no data are available to present any realistic picture of the share that each material holds of the durables market, whether by tonnage or by volume. The proportions in which particular materials substitute for one another vary widely from application to application: the choice may be based upon such diverse characteristics as strength, weight, thermal conductivity, hardness, workability, etc. There is no over-all unit of measurement that relates total expenditure for durables to total use of materials; consequently each of the three groups of materials must be looked at separately.

Wood has lost ground to both metals and plastics. Per dollar of furniture and fixtures output, the input of wood has been decreasing over the last twenty years, and this trend is likely to continue. This decline, however, will not be sharp enough to prevent population growth and income rise from producing a gain in wood use in furniture of about 75 per cent in the next twenty years, and another 60 per cent in the twenty years thereafter.

What little we know of the use of plastics in durables makes other increases seem puny. The output of moldings and extrusions—those plastic products most intimately connected with durables—has nearly tripled in the last decade alone, and per dollar of durables output has roughly doubled. Continuation of such growth would make plastics a prime durables raw material at the end of the century. For some kinds of durables—such as housewares and household appliances— plastics may even now have gone far ahead of metals, although adequate statistics are hard to come by. While there is virtually no possibility that the growth of plastics, rapid though it is, will run into any problems of materials adequacy, it is nonetheless important to determine the growth of plastics, since this conditions the growth of other materials such as metals or wood, where resource adequacy is open to question.

When it comes to metals, still the main constituent of durables, three different questions arise: (1) how much of the total value of durables is represented by their materials content and how is this proportion changing? (2) how does this value/materials ratio vary among different kinds of durables and what might be the effect of changes in the product mix? (3) what substitutions are taking place among the different metals?

The statistical record confirms the general impression that the value of machinery and equipment, whether used by business or households, is determined less and less by materials content and more and more by fabrication. The figures also show that, per dollar of product, the materials content of producer equipment is far greater than that of consumer durables. This contrast is partly due to the relatively greater use in consumer goods of the lighter, but more costly, non-ferrous metals; this makes for a low weight-to-value ratio. Another reason is that consumer durables must be far more acceptable in appearance and other features not involving performance. Thus the fabrication component tends to be higher in consumer durables.

There is ample reason to believe that the trend of decreasing materials content will continue. All kinds of equipment are becoming more and more complicated, thus requiring more and more labor input; the more complicated categories of equipment are becoming increasingly important parts of the total. More economical engineering and more miniaturization are cutting down the relative use of materials. Weight saving in one place results in weight saving elsewhere: printed circuits, for example, not only conserve copper wiring but decrease the size of the finished unit which houses the equipment; lighter-weight working parts for machinery mean lighter-weight structural members, and so on.

These tendencies, assumed to continue, will reduce the rate of materials consumption substantially below the rate at which expenditures for durables will be made. Total materials consumption for consumer durables, using steel's specific gravity as the common denominator, will not much more than triple between 1960 and 2000. This is in sharp contrast to a more than fivefold growth of *expenditures* for consumer durable goods. The discrepancy is less marked in the case of producer durables, where heavy weight continues as an essential factor in much equipment; here the growth in metal consumption will be over four times between 1960 and 2000, in contrast with a fivefold growth in expenditure. Figure 19 shows recent and projected use of metals in consumer and producer durables.

Within the metal family, the fastest growth should be of aluminum in consumer durables and to a less extent in producer durables. Because of its importance in electrical appli-

Figure 19. Use of metals in manufacture of durable goods, except transportation equipment.

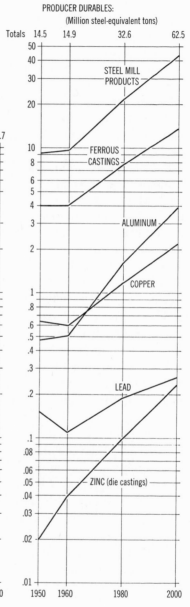

ances, copper should do relatively well in this particular field of application.

The Materials for Defense

A highly specialized segment of durables is military goods. The outstanding feature of this group is that while military expenditures represent nearly 10 per cent of the gross national product, only a rather small amount of raw materials and resources end up in "hardware," including military construction. Defense items are generally far ahead of civilian durables in their trend towards less and less materials content per dollar spent.

Included here, of course, are only peacetime military requirements and only those defense items that can be identified as end products. Material consumed in constructing plant and equipment which in turn may be used, directly or indirectly, for the production of military items is included with producer durables, and the impact of higher or lower defense expenditures upon the economy as a whole is allowed for in estimating the future gross national product and its components.

Even in nuclear warfare, the negligible role of materials as a component of defense would not change, for the great consumers of metal—munitions, arms, vehicles, and shipping —would be conspicuous by almost complete absence. However, projections used here comprise only the course of defense expenditures and their raw materials implications under continuing conditions of more or less cold war.

Despite all technological innovations, weaponry still is mostly a matter of metals, primarily steel, although chemicals and some other nonmetallics are also important. The specific applications, however, are far from static. Many minor materials, again mostly metals, fluctuate in relative importance. Thus arms still means metal, but metal no longer means arms. Only about 2 per cent of steel now finds direct defense application, and any future change will be toward a further decline. The relative significance of copper is about the same as that of steel. Aluminum, because of its use in airborne equipment, contains a somewhat larger defense quota: about 1 pound in 12 now goes into a defense application. But aluminum's future growth is not to be looked for in the defense area. Similarly, only small parts of the total production of lead, chromium, molybdenum, and tungsten go into direct defense uses. This situation is not likely to change. Nickel is important in spacecraft and aircraft equipment, especially in engines where special alloy steels must withstand enormously high temperatures, sometimes for prolonged periods, but large-scale use throughout the civilian economy keeps it from being a defense-dependent metal.

Titanium is highly dependent upon defense, and cadmium, cobalt, and some of the newer metals depend to a substantial degree on defense markets. However, in a field of such rapid development in which new materials emerge frequently, it is quite possible that even the metals that are now important may gradually be replaced by new types of plastics, ceramics, glass, or by combinations of these with metals.

Various factors will operate to keep defense fuel use from expanding as rapidly as fuel consumption in other uses. Even now, jet fuel represents at least one-half of all defense fuel, and has been the most dynamic of the different branches. But new types of fuel such as solid chemical fuels are becoming significant so that the consumption of jet fuel will not rise in proportion to expenditures on aircraft; and piston-powered aircraft will be disappearing, eliminating the demand for aviation gasoline. At the same time, though more slowly, naval fuel needs will decline as atom-powered ships take over. Finally, there is little reason to anticipate any rise in the use of fuel to power surface vehicles, such as automobiles, tanks, trucks, etc. On balance, therefore, defense consumption can be expected to become a shrinking segment of total fuel consumption.

Defense makes claims on resources other than metals and

fuel. Personnel has to be clothed; food is consumed; fixed installations have to be constructed; supply operations, instruction manuals, and correspondence consume paper, and so on. But in this study, such needs have been included with civilian requirements. The value of calculating metal and fuels separately lies mainly in demonstrating in detail how small in fact defense uses of these materials have become in modern military technology. Table 3 shows the use of major metals in defense.

Table 3. Major Metals in Military Goods Production

		(Thousand tons)
Metal	1960	2000
Carbon steel for:		
Aircraft, missiles, and spacecraft	153	375
Ships	207	464
Ordnance, vehicles, etc.	131	195
Electronics	53	128
Other procurement	153	764
Construction	297	1,030
Total	994	2,956
Alloy (incl. nickel stainless) steel for:		
Aircraft, missiles, and spacecraft	96	283
Ships, ordnance, vehicles, etc.	137	272
All other	16	52
Total	249	607
Aluminum for:		
Aircraft	59	18
Missiles and spacecraft	22	55
All other	30	80
Total	111	153
Copper and copper alloys	67	157

CONTAINERS AND PACKAGING

The Londoner wraps his fish and chips in a piece of newspaper. The Parisian grasps his bread firmly in the middle and carries it, afoot or on bicycle, unwrapped. The Roman transports his wine in his own container. The American buys everything wrapped, boxed, or bottled.

The United States is the heaviest consumer of packages and containers in the world, in terms both of volume and of value added, that is, the value of production exclusive of raw materials. Container and packaging manufacturing is our third largest industry, being topped only by automobiles and steel.

One need not endorse the underlying philosophy of the packaging age and one may not accept the fact that the degree of consumption in this field is one measure of the standard of living, but one cannot ignore the demand for materials for this use. What is of interest here is the rate of consumption of the materials that go to make up the many thousands of items in this category. And about the magnitude of this element there can be little dispute.

The packaging group involves items such as the cellophane wrapping of bread, the tube containing toothpaste or the paper bag holding cement. Despite the fact that the consumer encounters these items in small units and that there is usually no price tag, the value of shipments of all types of containers as they leave their place of manufacture amounts to some $12 billion annually. And that does not include the cost of filling, sealing, and otherwise processing the containers.

While it ranks as the third largest, this industry is greatly dispersed, the individual units are often small, and its raw materials sources very diverse. In terms of the value of shipments, a little less than half of the materials used is accounted for by paper and paperboard, about one-fifth by metal, not quite 10 per cent by glass, less than 4 per cent by wood, and a negligible fraction by textiles. Close to 20 per cent is accounted for by a variety of other materials among which plastics and aluminum foil are prominent. In terms of quantity, containers and packaging account for almost half of all paper consumption in the United States, about 10 per cent each of steel and aluminum consumption. Aided by the rapid rate at which Americans fill their trashcans and feed their incinerators, container and packaging consumption has grown at an annual rate of almost 5 per cent during the last twenty years—substantially faster than the gross national product. Some categories have grown even faster: paper packaging probably by nearly 6 per cent.

Use of tin cans has grown with the national tendency to consume more processed food—consumption of food, coffee, and malt beverages in cans or jars has increased over the past two decades from 115 pounds per person per year to over 180. The per capita use of aluminum in foil and collapsible tubes has more than tripled in the past ten years. A declining retail sales force in relation to the volume of goods sold, the spread of self-service and vending machines, and attempts to extend the life and improve the quality of perishable items have all increased the need for packaging. Added impetus is given by the emphasis on containers as a sales device. With most or all of these trends destined to continue, it follows that consumer goods packaging will also grow.

At the producer's end, that is, in manufacturing and distributing, consumption of containers has in general increased at a slower rate than at the consumer's end. There seem to be two principal reasons: industrial containers tend to be recirculated much more than consumer packages; and the trend in producer goods has been toward bulk handling, which means larger containers, or handling without containers altogether by tank barges, tank trucks, hopper vehicles or the like. Also, intrinsic quality is far more important than appearance at the manufacturing or wholesale level, and such matters as cleanliness, purity, etc., on the whole assume increasing importance as the later stages of processing and distribution are reached. Appearance counts for less: the purchaser of steel beams will not be deterred by evidence of surface rust, whereas the purchaser of a metal file or saw in a store will reject it if it looks rusty. Wheat may be swept off a truck, but an unwrapped roll may not be swept off the grocery shelf.

Substitutes and Combinations

Both consumers and producers tend to demand lighter-weight packaging: thinner walls, thinner covers, thinner films, lower densities. Sometimes this has involved a switch between materials; at other times it is the same material which has been so adapted, as in the case of glass. Hence, it is likely that quantities of raw materials required for containers will not increase as fast as the quantities of containers themselves.

Improved technology has also made container materials more perfect substitutes for one another. At one time certain types of containers had to be made of steel or wood or glass; this is now true to a diminishing degree. For example, corrugated paperboard boxing has so improved in strength and versatility in recent years as to have largely displaced heavier and costlier wooden crates; plastic bottles are substituting for glass ones; aluminum foil can be made sufficiently rigid to take the place of container board; aluminum cans can replace tinplate cans; cellophane derived from woodpulp is being replaced by films made of polyethylene or other hydrocarbon-derived substances.

Substitution, however, goes hand in hand with the use of two or three materials in a single kind of packaging: paper sheeting laminated with plastic film, aluminum foil bags lined with paper, rigid aluminum food containers equipped with paperboard tops and plastic windows, the coating of one metal with another. Thus, while one can be reasonably certain that per capita consumption of containers as a group will grow at a fairly predictable rate, the prospective consumption of different kinds of containers is obscure. The tin can, which involves large quantities of materials, is a good example. It has been with us for a long time, but its future depends upon technological progress which would allow food to be handled without any packaging at all, or at most with a plastic wrapper, through heat sterilization or irradiation. Then there is the question of the tin can proper versus the can made of aluminum. A third material is in full view: plastics.

Competition Among Materials

As Figure 20 shows, choice of materials for containers has changed rapidly and is expected to keep shifting in the future. The relative position of wood for containers is declining; part of its market has been lost to paperboard, part to metal. In one of its traditional markets, shipping fresh fruits and vegetables, the wooden crate has begun to be displaced by the paperboard box. There is every reason to believe that the relative share of wooden containers will shrink further.

Another victim of technology is glass. Its market has been invaded by plastics and paperboard, as cartons for milk and some soft drink containers. Other beverages—prominent among them beer—have shifted to the use of metal cans. Where glass containers can be recirculated, they have held out longest, but even there the disposable container, made of coated paper for milk, or metal for beer, has begun to prevail. Glass continues to be used for foods and liquids which would react corrosively with metal or have their taste impaired thereby, as for medicinals (though here the plastic container has made great progress), and where tradition is a strong factor, as in the retailing of wine. On the whole, however, glass is joining wood as one of the packaging materials of decreasing importance.

The future of paper as a packaging material is interesting: at one end of the flexibility scale it finds its domain invaded by plastics; at the other end, it has become sufficiently rigid to compete with wood and metal. As a whole, the use of

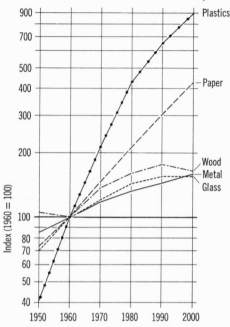

Figure 20. The changing composition of containers and packaging materials.

paper for containers should grow at about the same rate as the gross national product.

The fastest growth is expected for the transparent films, especially those not made of cellophane. The fivefold growth in poundage projected from 1960 to 1980, and an additional though much less rapid growth thereafter, would take plastic transparent film consumption to more than 1½ million tons per year by the end of the century, as compared with less than 150,000 tons in 1960. An equally rapid growth can be expected where more rigid types of plastic are used, such as bottles, boxes, jars, etc. A later chapter will discuss the question of whether this rapid growth will have a significant bearing on the adequacy of petroleum and natural gas, the basic resources from which most noncellulosic films are derived.

TOTAL DEMAND FOR METALS

Having looked at the future demand for major metals in the principal metal-consuming sections of the economy—construction, transportation, durables, military goods, containers and packaging—it now remains to round out the picture by accounting for all consumption of these metals. This task involves complex calculations and statistical approximations. It also means making adjustments for alloys, the use of which is increasing both in the ferrous and nonferrous metal industries. Finally, in order to gain a more realistic view of the magnitude of new metal required by the economy, it involves accounting for the reuse of scrap—products that have already been in use or that constitute waste in the production process itself.

Scrap—A Special Kind of Resource

Requirements for the metal content of a finished product need not be satisfied entirely from newly-mined metal, but can be met in part from scrap. In some industries a very large part comes from scrap. Perhaps the most extreme case is that of lead. Not only is a substantial amount of lead recovered from scrap, but most of it comes from a single source—junked automotive batteries. Scrap sources for other metals are usually more diversified. Old motor windings furnish copper; so do pipes and tubing, kettles, boilers, gaskets, and automobile radiators. Junked automobiles, industrial and agricultural machinery, and the borings, punchings, stampings and other leftovers from fabricated metal processing furnish scrap for steelmaking. Figure 21 shows the approximate flow of ferrous metals through the economy—from iron ore and obsolete scrap to finished products and the eventual return of a part of the finished products as scrap into new production.

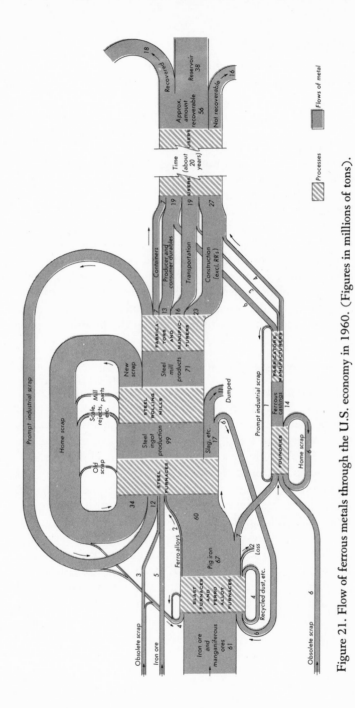

Figure 21. Flow of ferrous metals through the U.S. economy in 1960. (Figures in millions of tons).

The Dynamic Outlook for Metals

Growth in metals consumption is one of the best single measures of man's material progress. Since the beginning of the nineteenth century, U.S. population and income growth have been accompanied by a growth of iron and steel production from less than 100,000 tons to about 100 million tons a year today. Per capita consumption rose from about 30 pounds to around half a ton, which is roughly double the per capita consumption that prevails in most of the industrialized countries of Western Europe. In general, the United States accounts for about one-third to one-half of the non-Communist world's total consumption of all the principal metals.

In spite of recent increasing use of plastics and other synthetics, and the possible future use of relatively greater quantities of stone, gravel, and cement, it is improbable that the relative importance of metals will diminish greatly between now and the year 2000. Certainly, absolute growth will continue to be large: 3.1 per cent per year over the next forty years, compared with 3.3 per cent in the past forty years. Thus, as in the past, future annual growth is somewhat less than the anticipated growth of the gross national product (3.8 per cent), but about twice as large as the future growth in population (1.55 per cent). Put differently, metal use per capita in the United States will continue to rise, while use per dollar of gross national product will decline.

One of the reasons for the continued dynamic outlook for the consumption of metals is their versatility. Metals can withstand the influence of time, weather, and large loads, but they can also fulfill the modest function of a paperclip. Some can withstand strong corrosive chemicals; some are excellent conductors of electricity. Metals that can retain their characteristics under intense heat have been developed, along with others that will not succumb to severe cold. Metals are being used for rocket fuel; indeed, in the field of outer space we may see more and more of a topsy-turvy situation in which metals are burned as propellants and petroleum made into plastic makes up structural parts.

Nonmetals versus Metals

Recent advances in developing new synthetic materials— from the most flexible to the most rigid—are enabling synthetics to compete with aluminum foil as wrapping material, with steel pipe, with steel and other metals as basic components of consumer and producer durables and as components of spacecraft.

While expensive on a weight basis, synthetics are far cheaper than metals on a volume basis. For example, steel weighs about three-tenths of a pound per cubic inch. Most resins, the basic material of plastics, weigh less than five-hundredths of a pound per cubic inch. Thus where volume is the appropriate measure of comparison, a resin may cost up to six times as much per pound as a metal and still retain price competitiveness. There are usually additional factors that favor the new substances: ease of fabrication, greater flexibility in incorporating specific qualities, ease of handling, and so on.

The future division of the materials market between metals and plastics will depend on the interplay of several factors. Both the capability of the synthetics and their prices as compared to metal will enter the picture.

Goaded by the growing aggressiveness of the synthetics, metals have been making themselves more competitive, both in terms of characteristics and price. This has undoubtedly helped to slow down the rate at which metals have yielded ground to the synthetics. At the same time, it has, interestingly enough, retarded the growth of metals, considered purely in terms of tonnage. One of the ways in which metals, particularly steel, have responded to the challenge of the synthetics has been to turn out lighter products. An outstanding example is the tin can. It is also true, however, of pipes of all kinds, panels used in large buildings, and so on. In the steel industry, output has been conventionally measured by the tonnage of the undifferentiated, unfinished steel as it is drawn from the open hearth or other type of steel furnace and solidifies into ingots. Since one ingot ton now results in more finished products than it did only a few years ago, its usefulness as a measure of growth in steel production is beginning to wane. It follows that the less rapid ingot tonnage growth projected for the future gives an exaggerated impression of the retardation in metal consumption growth.

Quantitatively, the role of plastics is still relatively small. It is difficult to be precise, but in 1960 the plastics that are directly competitive with metallic materials may have totaled in the neighborhood of 1 million tons; certainly no higher than 1½ million tons. This compares with steel ingot production near the 100-million-ton level. Again, however, comparison by tonnage may be inappropriate. On a volumetric basis, the comparison would be more like 6 to 9 million tons of plastics versus 100 million tons of steel, plus a few million tons of the remaining metals.

Metals versus Metals

In addition to competing with other materials, metals also compete vigorously among themselves. The different growth rates projected for the future reflect anticipation of substitution in various uses, as well as the different rates of growths of these uses themselves.

As one would expect, aluminum shows the fastest rate of growth in the future, as in the postwar period. Aluminum consumption as a share of total metal consumption (when all metals are combined in terms of their relative volume rather than weight) is projected to rise from less than 6 per cent in 1960 to about 17 per cent by the end of the century. Copper and zinc too are projected to rise somewhat faster than iron and steel, each doubling its consumption between 1960 and 1980, and not quite doubling it again in the twenty years thereafter. Iron and steel consumption, the basic point of reference in the metal picture, is projected to rise a little less than three times between 1960 and 2000. Only lead and tin, among the traditional metals, are projected to rise more slowly. The increase in lead consumption between 1960 and 2000 is not quite two and a half times, and tin consumption is projected to just about double in the forty years ahead. The reason for the slow rise in tin is, to a large extent, the declining importance of the tin can, and the declining amount of tin used in each can, brought about largely by the sharp competition to which this type of container has been subjected. Figure 22 shows projected consumption of major metals.

The above comparisons are made in terms of tonnage to lay the groundwork of projected demand for a later determination of the adequacy of materials resources. Tonnage, as has been stated, is not necessarily the best indicator of an industry's progress, and care must be taken, therefore, not to use these growth rates as a basis for judging the future well-being, profitability, or dynamism of an industry. As products incorporate growing amounts of labor, especially skilled labor, and less and less material, especially of the heavy kind, the account cast in tonnage becomes a poor guide to a meaningful judgment of commercial success.

PAPER

The largest end use of paper is packaging. This has already been discussed, as has the use of building board and paper in construction. Among the other classes that contribute to the total demand for paper, by far the largest is newsprint, followed by other printing papers (see Figure 23).

Americans use paper in a prodigal manner. The weight of American newspapers—not only the Sunday editions—has frequently been commented on by foreign visitors, conditioned to newspapers of rarely more than sixteen pages. Most of the other classes of commercial papers are used with similar

Figure 22. Projected use of major metals: a general rise at varying rates.

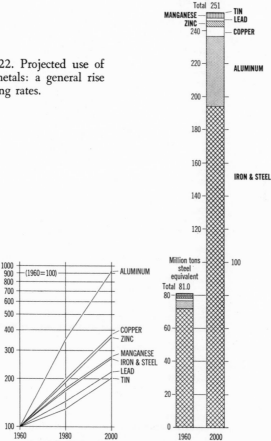

lavishness. One American may consume more paper in one trip to the supermarket than an inhabitant of East or South Asia in several months.

Gross annual consumption of paper and paperboard in this country is now approaching one ton per family. Total volume per year is nearly 40 million tons, or nearly half the amount

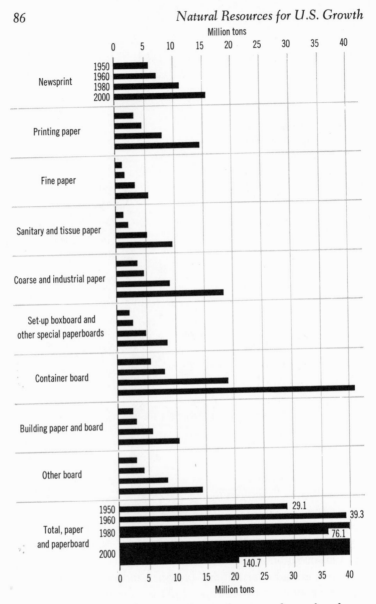

Figure 23. Projected increases in use of paper and paperboard.

of steel used in the economy. In 1950 it was not quite 30 million tons, and in 1929 not even 15 million tons. Of the total, nearly half goes for containers and packaging, not quite 20 per cent for newsprint, and a little over 10 per cent for other printing paper. The remainder goes into other uses and is made up of fine paper (for writing, typing, etc.), sanitary and tissue paper, coarse and industrial paper, and various types of boxboard and paperboard.

Considering the current high consumption levels, one might well question the further scope for market expansion of paper above that implied by sheer population growth. Yet the same argument might have been made five, ten, or twenty years ago, and each time events would have proved it wrong. Only the depression of the thirties and the war years checked the long-term rise of per capita consumption of paper and board.

Newsprint has had a long-term growth rate appreciably higher than that of the population. Daily circulation of newspapers has been increasing, and so has average number of pages per issue, with the growth of advertising and editorial linage. Until recently, newspapers averaged a ratio of about six pages of advertising to four of nonadvertising space. Closer spacing of columns, smaller print, and narrow margins have failed to offset the upward trend of newsprint. Unless all present trends should cease, which is an unlikely development, one may expect some further increase in per capita consumption of newsprint.

While projections have been geared to requirements for domestic paper needs, prospects for expanding export markets for a number of commercial grades of paper appear quite favorable. Considering the difference between per capita paper consumption in this country and the rest of the world, one may expect international flow of paper to expand sharply in the future, as overseas and particularly European paper requirements outstrip the productive capacity of European and especially Scandinavian mills. Paper output in the United

States and the concomitant consumption of woodpulp are therefore likely to rise somewhat above the levels here projected in terms of domestic requirements. The difficulty of obtaining data and making meaningful projections of consumption abroad, however, have prevented the translation of this anticipation into numbers. It is assumed that the United States will continue to meet a substantial portion of its paper needs through imports of newsprint from Canada, which have to be taken into account when estimating demand for wood by U.S. paper mills.

TOTAL DEMAND FOR FOREST PRODUCTS

Requirements for construction, containers, newsprint, textiles, heating and many other uses—most of which are discussed separately elsewhere in this book—all contribute to the total demand for forest products. These can be measured in board feet of lumber, square feet of veneer, cords of fuelwood, or tons of pulp, but they cannot be compared in magnitude or added. A common denominator is found by going back a step farther and expressing them in terms of cubic volume of roundwood, which represents the portions of a tree of sufficient diameter and length to be commercially useful. This produces not just an estimate of total demand, but one that can be related to the probable supply from the nation's forest resources.

Conversion of logs into sawn products or veneer entails waste, on the average, of something like 40 or 50 per cent of the original volume of the log. A considerable part of this residue is used for other purposes such as fuel, pulp, or more recently particle board. Insofar as they substitute for roundwood, residues support a larger production of wood products per unit of timber cut than would be possible if all the raw material for each wood product had to come from timber cut for the specific purposes. Since not all residues can be used for all purposes, and since it is not always economical to substitute other fuels for mill waste, the limits upon by-product use are perhaps narrower than this high percentage figure would lead one to suspect. However, it is assumed that present trends toward greater use of mill residues can continue for at least the rest of the century. This finds practical expression in the assumption that a declining share of pulpwood will come from roundwood cut specifically for that purpose. Should this expectation not be borne out, projected roundwood requirements would of course be too low.

In terms of roundwood, saw logs for production of lumber represent about half of all timber products. Next comes pulpwood, which accounts for about one-fourth of all roundwood. Then follows fuelwood, which has been rapidly declining in importance, and now represents only a little more than 10 per cent. Veneer logs—the source of plywood—and miscellaneous timber products together account for the balance of not quite 15 per cent. Much of the "miscellaneous" category, such as railroad ties, mine timbers, and fence poles, faces a declining market, like fuelwood.

In terms of end products or use, construction and paper together account for nearly all the expected increase in consumption between now and the end of the century—12 billion and 7 billion cubic feet respectively, out of a total increase of 21 billion cubic feet. In mere size these two swamp such other uses as containers, furniture and fixtures, etc. In 1960, for example, 75 per cent of all lumber and most of the softwood plywood was used in construction. Since lumber alone accounts for about half of all timber products and pulpwood represents about one-quarter, easily 70 per cent ends up in the construction and paper industries. Recent and projected requirements for the principal kinds of timber products are shown in Figure 24, in the common denominator of billions of cubic feet.

Total timber consumption by the end of the century is projected as not quite three times as high as in 1960, 32 as against 11.5 billion cubic feet. However, there is much diver-

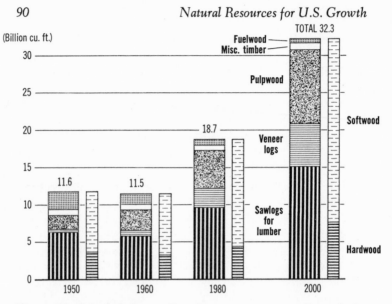

Figure 24. Principal forms of timber consumption, with totals for softwood and hardwood.

sity among major classes of products. The demand for veneer logs, the source of plywood, is projected as rising sevenfold in the next forty years, and consumption of pulpwood as increasing about three and a half times between 1960 and 2000. This is balanced by a more moderate rise in sawlogs and miscellaneous timber, and a decline in fuelwood. All this assumes that forest products will be available at prices no higher than those suggested by past trends.

The projected rapid increase in plywood, especially the softwood variety, as compared with lumber carries an interesting implication. Since they have greater strength, thinner plywood sections may substitute for heavier lumber, a significant saving in the volume of trees to be cut to fill the same purpose. The actual figures projected imply a saving on that basis of some 4 billion cubic feet of roundwood annually by the end of the century, or more than 10 per cent of total projected timber use. To the extent, however, that specific portions of the tree are useful for lumber and not for plywood production, these hypothetical savings would be diminished.

THE USES OF ENERGY

Without energy, other resources would be of little avail. We consume energy in the home to stay warm in winter and cool in summer, to heat water, to cook meals, to operate vacuum cleaners and washing machines, to power electrical razors or hi-fi sets. We use it to move people and things: it drives father to work, children to school, and satellites into outer space. It provides heat to melt ore, power to drive printing presses, steam to generate electricity. In more recent times, fuel commodities have become increasingly important raw materials for a whole new family of products: the chemical starting point for fertilizers, pesticides, medicines, soap, paint. As we have seen, fibers, durables, and containers all draw in varying but increasing proportions on fuel materials.

Industry is by far the largest user of energy, accounting for better than one-third of total use; transportation and residential use each account for about one-fifth. Jointly these three users consume 75 per cent of all energy. The remainder is divided among commercial uses, such as in stores, offices, etc.; agriculture, which accounts for surprisingly little; the military; all manner of public consumption by government or quasi-governmental agencies; and the use of energy materials for the production of asphalt, wax, and other nonenergy uses. To all these must be added losses in the course of production, transportation, and distribution.

How Much Now and Later?

In 1960 the U.S. economy consumed some 45 million billion (45×10^{15}) British thermal units (Btu). This is hardly the kind of figure designed to conjure up a useful image, even when one knows that a British thermal unit is the amount of energy needed to raise the temperature of one pound of water by one degree Fahrenheit. It becomes a little more comprehensible if one thinks of this magnitude as approaching the energy inherent in about 2 billion tons of coal— equal to about five years' U.S. coal production.

The question to which answers must be found is not only how much energy will the American economy be needing twenty or forty years from now, but how much of this energy will be supplied by coal, oil, gas, falling water, nuclear fission or fusion, or by some entirely new source.

There is no satisfactory shortcut to estimating future energy requirements. We know, of course, how much energy we have been using in recent years and in what combination, but no pattern reveals itself as a key to the future.

The great swings of the past are plain enough—from wood to coal to oil and gas (see Figure 25). But there is no warrant for simply extending the trend lines beyond 1960. The projections in the chart are built up from separate considerations of the outlook for different uses of energy and their possible effects on each other. On the basis of these inquiries, which are sketched briefly in the next few pages, it appears that by the year 2000 the nation's total consumption of energy in Btu's may be nearly three times what it was in 1960.

Heating the Home

Space heating is one of the largest single categories of energy consumption, and constitutes by far the largest home use. As in food consumption, there are certain limits: few want house temperatures much above 80° or much below 70°. But there are no statistics to measure anything that could be called the "average heating requirement" of the American household. However, a crude average of the energy needed for space heating may be stated as being in the neighborhood of 70 million Btu per household per year. Allowing for inefficiencies in burning, this is the equivalent of some 4-5 tons of coal, or 800-900 gallons of oil, or 90,000 cubic

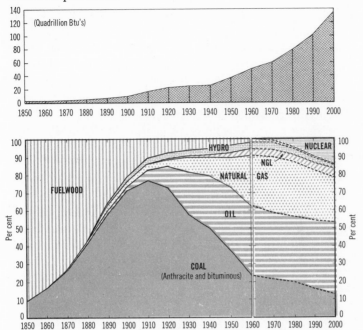

Figure 25. Past and projected energy use: rising total consumption and a shifting pattern of supply.

feet of gas. The oil equivalent is some 20 per cent larger than the amount of gasoline used annually by the average passenger car. In other words, it takes about as much fuel to warm an "average" home in an "average" location during the winter as it takes to drive the family car for a little over a year.

The migration of Americans to the South and West, generally to warmer climates, favors a decline in average heating needs, as do improvements in insulation practices, which can reduce fuel consumption by 30 to 50 per cent. Offsetting this would be an expected increase in the number of adequately heated houses, and the adding of heating equipment to houses not now provided with any form of heating. On the basis of a number of such trends—not all pulling in the same direction—it can be assumed that average energy consumption for house heating will increase for some time to come; but that after 1980 there will be a decline.

Not allowed for in these assumptions are any radical innovations such as solar heating or long-distance transmission of centrally generated heat, or any sustained substantial shift from single-family dwellings to apartment dwellings, which would result both in reduced heating needs and in a different pattern of heat sources.

Gas and oil now heat over 80 per cent of all households, having taken over the job from coal, just as coal at one time displaced wood. The most striking advances have been made by natural gas. In little more than a decade the number of gas customers for heating has nearly tripled: from 7½ million in 1949 to over 21 million at the end of 1960. Prospects are that growth will continue, but at a slower pace, as a larger share of the heating market is captured. More recently, the electric utilities have entered the fray, and the struggle has become one of gas versus oil versus electricity. To the extent that coal remains the main fuel for generating electricity, the spread of electricity signals the re-entry of coal into the home heating market.

Since most people buy ready-built homes, with heating systems installed, the key to the choice of heating systems probably lies more with the builder than the eventual resident, making the cost of the original equipment a more important criterion than the cost of operation. Because of the simplicity of the gas burner, the absence of storage requirements, and the reduced need for piping and wiring, gas heating equipment has had a clear cost advantage over oil, and in addition the gas industry has successfully merchandized gas heating.

The price of fuel seems to have played a secondary role. Since the end of the 1940's, when gas heating began its rapid expansion, gas prices have risen greatly compared to coal or oil. But in late 1960 oil marketers estimated that the price of gas would have to rise "another 30 per cent" before fuel costs would begin to affect the choice of heating equipment. Absence of gas pipelines in those parts of the nation most remote from gas fields seems to have been a principal factor in holding back even further expansion. Emergence of Canadian gas and its export to the northern and western states in newly constructed pipelines is likely to change that picture.

A government survey made in 1956 found that gas heating equipment was then being installed in 72 per cent of all new single-family dwellings. Oil-burning equipment, which had captured one-third of the new housing market in the 1940's, had been cut back to about 20 per cent by 1956, while coal heating had practically vanished from new housing.

Indications are that electricity may be to gas what gas has been to oil and oil to coal. Among the principal advantages claimed for electric heating by its proponents are absence of piping, savings in construction because of absence of chimney and flues, cleanliness, individual room control, more even temperature conditions, silent operation, and space saving. Because of its high operating cost, electrical heating equipment is usually installed only if the house is insulated far more thoroughly than is normally the case. This apparent drawback may eventually turn into an advantage, especially where air conditioning is added.

It has been suggested in the past that by 1980 there may be 29 million electrically heated homes. A more modest estimate released in 1963 by an advisory committee to the Federal Power Commission's National Power Survey found 19 million electrically heated homes by 1980 to be a more acceptable working hypothesis. The figure adopted in RFF's estimates is closer to 10 million. This compares with barely 1 million electrically heated homes in 1960. Obviously, there is room here for controversy.

Figure 26 shows where balancing of the various trends would take us in the future. Salient features are a slowdown in the expansion of natural gas heating, eventually leading to a decline in its share, a continuing decline in the importance of oil heating, with its share cut in half between 1960 and 2000, virtual disappearance of coal heating in the course of the next forty years, and an increase in electrical heating that would boost its share to 30 per cent of the heating market at the end of the century.

Since we have an idea of the average amount of heating required, as well as of the efficiency with which fuel input is converted into heat output in the home, it is not difficult to translate market shares into physical requirements for energy. Only in the case of electricity will much depend upon the specific devices. These include not only the conventional heater in which metal, usually in the form of wires, is heated through resistance and which produces as much heat as the energy that is put into it, but also the heat pump. The latter transfers heat from or into the house, depending on whether it operates on the cooling or heating cycle. It can produce two or three times as much heat as the thermal input of the electricity that powers the pump. However, because of initial

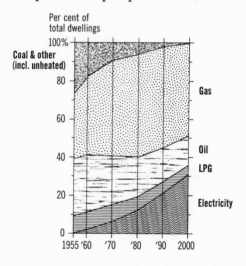

Figure 26. How dwellings are heated.

technical difficulties, high cost, and the fact that heating and cooling loads have to be fairly evenly matched to exploit its efficiency, it has been assumed that not until the end of the century will the heat pump have captured a major share of the electric heating market.

Noteworthy changes in rank of the quantities of heat supplied by the principal fuels between now and the end of the century are: gas rising from practical equality with oil in 1960 to a position in the year 2000 where gas consumption is nearly three times that of oil; electricity—measured in terms of fuel input to generate it—overtaking oil after 1980, and by the year 2000 supplying over half as much heat as gas.

Domestic Cooking, Cooling, Lighting, etc.

Not more than one-third of all natural gas used in the home goes to uses other than space heating, and probably no more than one-fifth of oil is so used. Cooking and water heating are the large-scale consumers, and both have had growing competition from electricity. In both instances, gas has been giving way slowly, oil rapidly. There is not at present any reason to anticipate a change in that trend, though much will depend on the success of electric utilities in penetrating the space-heating market. In that event, the "all-electric" home could lead to a much faster displacement of nonelectric appliances than is depicted in Table 4 which shows the projected spread of ranges and water heaters—and their energy demand—and Table 5 which shows the energy source pattern for all nonheating uses.

In lighting, the consumer has shown himself to be far more conservative than the utility man would like. He may have become less intent on turning off the lights when he leaves a room; he may now use a 75-watt bulb where he once used a 60- or 40-watt bulb; he may also have a few more floor lamps. But he and his family spend many hours during the week watching television in one room with minimum illumination; perhaps they go out more often and have longer and

Table 4. Use of Energy for Cooking and Water Heating in the Home

	1951	1960	1980	2000
Number of ranges in use per household	0.84	1.05	1.16	1.20
Per cent of ranges in use:				
Electric	24	32	51	62
Gas	76	68	49	38
Energy consumed per year:				
Electricity (bil. kwh)	n.a.	21	43	59
Gas (bil. cu. ft.)	n.a.	346	343	338
Number of water heaters in use per household	0.44	0.61	0.85	1.00
Per cent of water heaters in use:				
Electric	25	30	41	56
Gas	75	70	59	44
Energy consumed per year:				
Electricity (bil. kwh)	n.a.	45	120	240
Gas (bil. cu. ft.)	n.a.	565	919	1,013

n.a. Not available.

Table 5. The Role of Different Energy Sources in the Home (except for Heating)

			(Per cent)
Energy source	1960	1980	2000
Gas	27.7	28.9	22.4
Oil	14.1	5.8	3.5
Liquid petroleum gas (LPG)	3.6	2.4	1.7
Electricity	54.6	62.9	72.4
All sources	100.0	100.0	100.0

more frequent vacations. Whatever the reasons, lighting is apparently not one of the fast-growing outlets for power consumption in the home. Annual increases of 25 kilowatt-hours per capita seem to have been the average in the past two decades. Air conditioning, on the other hand, may be expected to become a standard item of home comfort, and central air conditioning should make an increasing contribution to total electricity consumption. Lower rates for electrical heating and an improved heat pump that will serve to heat in winter and cool in summer could promote the use of electricity for space heating. It could also stimulate increased marketing of gas air conditioning. Indeed, it would not be wrong to say that the future battle between natural gas and electricity as a source of household energy will be fought in the heating and air conditioning field.

A large number of electrical appliances now in use may be expected to find greater acceptance: home freezers, clothes dryers, etc. Spread of the freezer, with its rather high power demands, would rapidly raise domestic electricity use. Then there are what the industry calls "phantom" appliances—those not now in use or not even on the drawing board—which will undoubtedly appear and be used in growing numbers. The residential uses of electricity are shown in Figure 27. The "miscellaneous" category in the chart (which shows a substantial growth) includes the future use of appliances both in existence but not separately projected, and "phantom."

Commercial Uses of Energy

Commercial energy consumption accounts for around 9 per cent of the nation's total energy use. Among the consumers are stores, warehouses, offices, hotels, clubs, apartment houses, etc. Projections of the shares of individual energy sources in commercial uses are shown in Figure 28. These are based on the assumption of a continuing close relationship between residential and commercial uses.

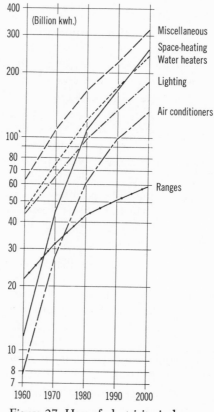

Figure 27. Uses of electricity in homes.

Both coal and fuel oil have had greater staying power in the commercial field than in residential use. It is unlikely that this will substantially change in the future. By the same token, it will be more difficult for electricity to assert itself in the commercial market. Certainly this will be true for space heating. The typical household appliances also play a much smaller role in commercial establishments. A recent development is the independent generation of electricity in large housing developments, schools, etc., fueled either by oil or

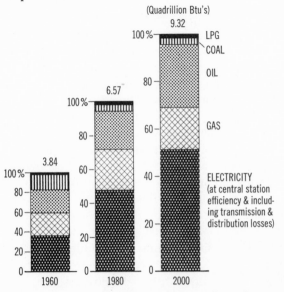

Figure 28. How different forms of energy may share the commercial market.

natural gas. As yet it is too early to judge its competitive strength but it could hold down expansion of utility-supplied electricity in commercial use.

Industry—Energy's Largest User

Industry takes more than 35 per cent of the total energy used in the United States. Fuels are used as either furnace or steam heat, to melt, boil, distill, mix, separate, or otherwise transform materials. Electric power is used similarly in some applications—in electric metal furnaces, for example—but mostly it is used to drive machinery. Today, close to 30 per cent of all energy used in industry is electric power, up from slightly over 20 per cent in 1939. Indications are that this rising tendency will continue through the rest of the century, giving electricity nearly 40 per cent of industry's total energy consumption market in the year 2000.

In view of the importance of electricity in automation, the persistent dominance of nonelectrical energy is noteworthy. Primarily responsible is the large amount of heat needed in processing metals and crude oil, which means the persistence of furnace and steam heat as one of industry's prime uses of energy. Without the fuel burned in metal and oil processing, the energy market would be more nearly evenly divided between electric power and process heat.

A continuing tendency is the declining use of energy, in all forms, per unit of industrial output. This can be measured by comparing an index of industrial production with total energy consumption by industry. In the twenty-five years between the 1929 and the 1954 Census of Manufactures, energy per unit of industrial output declined by nearly 30 per cent. This decline is estimated as continuing at about the same rate in the next twenty years. The decline between 1980 and 2000, on the other hand, should be somewhat slower. Figure 29 shows this trend.

A significant technical change clearly in prospect is the industrial application of nuclear energy. Nuclear process heat (leaving aside, for the moment, nuclear generation of electric power, dealt with later), generated in industrial plants or groups of plants, is a definite likelihood in many industries. However, it is difficult at this time to form any judgments concerning application of nuclear processes in any branch of industry. Perhaps, as more attention is devoted to developing economical small power reactors, design of an efficient small nonpower reactor will advance. The potential market for this kind of nuclear energy is impressive. It was estimated several years ago that at the cost level of 70 cents per million Btu, which reactor design was just approaching at that time, there was an industrial heat market (focusing on new equipment only) in the United States for the equivalent of some 6 million tons of coal per year. With nuclear equipment that could produce heat at no more than 60 cents, the market for

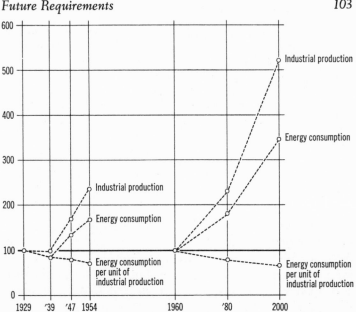

Figure 29. Energy use in industry: consumption per unit of output will continue to fall.

new nuclear equipment might be the equivalent of eight or ten times that tonnage.

Also likely is the use of nuclear energy for transforming material by imparting desirable qualities through irradiation. Entire new industries may emerge from such applications, and some atomic scientists believe this will be the most exciting aspect of nuclear growth. At present, however, we are at the very beginning of this branch of industrial energy use, and the projections do not therefore allow for its use.

Past changes in industrial energy consumption typically have been in the direction of lower unit consumption for fuel use other than electricity, and higher unit consumption for electric power. Year-to-year changes have not generally been large—ordinarily not exceeding 1 or 2 per cent. Over a span of forty years, of course, such changes are significant.

The increase in electric power consumption is the result of three quite separate tendencies: better than average growth of the more power-intensive industries or branches of industries; a shift toward more power-intensive processes within industries, as in chemicals; and the expansion of the "electric way of doing things" into existing nonelectric processes or the complete replacement of nonelectric by electrical fabrication methods.

To illustrate, electric power consumption per unit of output has been rising for the past decade in the food, beverage, and tobacco industries. On the assumption that this rise is related to the continuing introduction of processing and handling by electricity, this trend will continue. Unit power requirements have been lowered in the production of primary aluminum with improvements in the efficiency of the electrolytic process, but the rapidly expanding use of aluminum has meant that more than half the increase in electrical power consumption by industry as a whole is accounted for by aluminum production. Among the metals, only titanium outdistances aluminum as a consumer of electric power per unit, and a shift to this metal in the future would similarly raise electricity consumption by way of a change in the "product mix." Projected consumption of electricity by the industries that are its principal users is shown in Figure 30.

There is a great deal of basic research to be done on the change in the mix of products—especially within specific industries—that has contributed to larger power consumption, both in the development and refinement of historical data and in speculating about future trends. For example, the chemical industry is one of the large consumers of energy—but changing processes, end-uses and new combinations of basic materials make it difficult to project energy consumption for chemicals.

The statistical difficulties are multiplied when one wants to estimate the burning of fuels for direct application, rather than via the electricity detour. Pertinent data on an industry-

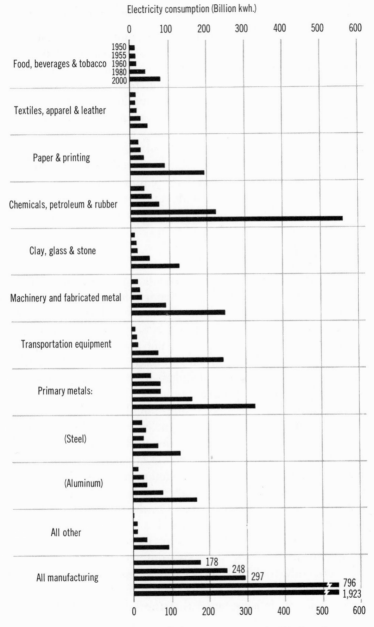

Figure 30. Consumption of electricity in principal industries.

by-industry basis are difficult both to find and to interpret. The past record indicates, however, as has been stated, that consumption of nonelectric energy per unit of output in industry has been steadily declining, partly as the corollary of increased electrical energy consumption, partly from increased efficiency in burning fuels. Assumed for the future is the continuation of this declining trend—except for oil refining, where the greatly increased product differentiation and the intensified breakup of the petroleum hydrocarbons into lighter and lighter fractions require more energy. Primary metals, on the other hand, can be expected to share in the general decline in the use of nonelectric energy per unit of output.

The Fuels That Industry Uses

Industry—excluding primary metals manufacturing, which relies mainly on coal, and petroleum refining, which burns both by-products of the refinery process and large amounts of natural gas—is seen to rely for close to 50 per cent of its direct fuel needs on natural gas, not above 30 per cent on coal, and for the balance on oil and natural gas liquids. When metals and refineries are included, gas and coal contribute 36 and 38 per cent respectively.

How long will the recent but rapidly developing trend toward natural gas continue? In or near coal-producing regions, of course, coal will be the principal energy source for industry. Anything done by the coal industry and railroads or other means of transportation to lower the cost of coal to the consumer will further push out the borders of regions relying primarily on coal. On the other hand, natural gas lines have continued to expand, and in many industries where energy is a small cost factor the convenience offered by gas versus coal can offset cost differences. The future of oil as an industrial fuel depends to a large extent on public policy decisions on the import of cheap residual oil.

On balance, it is assumed that the sale of natural gas to

industry will rise farther, though much more slowly; that the share of coal will decline farther; and that there will be a slight decline in the share of oil. Figure 31 shows the projected shares of the different fuels in industry.

Energy in Agriculture

The small percentage of total energy that can be tagged as being consumed in farming is largely in the form of liquid fuels for driving trucks, tractors, and other farm machinery. Coal and gas consumption by agriculture is not separately recorded. Estimates by those who have looked into it put gas use at less than 1 per cent of total gas sales. Similarly, consumption of electricity specifically for operating irrigation

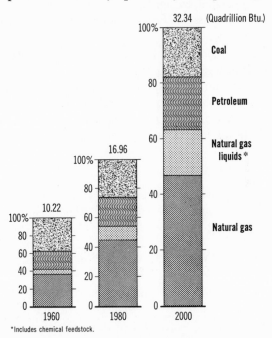

Figure 31. Sources of energy for industrial use (except electricity) and rise of total consumption.

and drainage equipment is estimated in the neighborhood of 1 per cent of all current electricity generated. Altogether, agriculture probably accounts for not much over 3 per cent of energy consumption in the economy as a whole.

From data collected sporadically, one can conclude that agriculture uses about 10 per cent of total consumption of liquid petroleum products. This, however, includes fuel consumed not only for productive purposes, but also for driving automobiles in the everyday pursuits of a normal household, for space heating, cooking, etc. With this qualification, agriculture qualifies as an important customer of liquid fuel today, but it will probably be less so in the future. Recent years have witnessed a gradual slowdown in the growth of farm implements operated by agricultural producers. Numbers of tractors and combines on farms, for example, have begun to decline.

There are no conclusive data as to any parallel trends in liquid fuel consumption. A smaller stock of machines may do the same amount of work or even more. But it is difficult to imagine how a slackening in the growth of liquid fuel consumption could be avoided and agriculture not become a factor of declining importance.

Sources of Electrical Energy

Before the demand for energy by various users can be compared with supply, one additional step must be taken. Much of the energy demanded will be electricity. But there does not exist any "total stock of available electricity" that can be compared directly with so many billion kilowatt-hours that we think will be used. Electricity requirements must therefore be reduced to the primary source from which this power is derived—that is, to a fuel, conventional or unconventional, or to falling water. When these amounts are added to the demands for liquid fuel for transportation, coal for melting iron ore, natural gas for heating homes, etc., aggregates of primary energy materials are arrived at which can be usefully compared with availability of those resources.

What are the ingredients that must go into such a projection of the share of primary energy sources in the generation of electricity? There is the past record. There is the role of nuclear energy, as yet difficult to discern. There are impending technological improvements in transportation of conventional fuels, especially coal which has been under strong competitive pressure. There is the excellent possibility of significant innovations in the engineering of power generation, using conventional fuels in new ways. And there are altogether novel conversion methods, still commercially in their infancy but potentially of a kind to upset the traditional patterns of electric power generation.

All these work eventually through the price mechanism. But in addition, these ingredients must be looked at not nationally, but from the local angle. Transportation cost and locational advantages figure prominently in the energy picture. Attention to regional differences in economic growth, as well as to regional differences in the cost of the various primary energy commodities, is indispensable in any appraisal.

Outstanding in the record of the past dozen years or so is the great increase in the share of natural gas as an electric utility fuel. Figure 32 shows the changing pattern in the postwar years. There is divided opinion on how much longer this trend can continue. Regional limitations alone make it likely that the rate of increase will soon slow down substantially—there are simply too many areas in which gas will continue to be too expensive to compete with other energy sources in the generation of electricity.

The same reasoning applies to a portion of coal- and oil-burning generation. Large cost-reducing improvements would have to take place in the transportation of coal to make it competitive in, say, the vicinity of Houston, Texas. Although there has been some discussion of pipelining coal from western

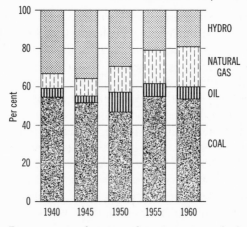

Figure 32. Past sources of energy for generation of electricity by utilities.

mountain states to California, this would seem to be less likely than increasing rail shipments.

In line with this approach one can fix certain rockbottom amounts of electrical energy that are mortgaged to one or the other of the conventional fuels. This reduces the area of uncertainty in the remaining regions in which costs of different fuels permit various alternatives. Here the past trend is of considerable importance, at least for the near term.

Most difficult of all to deal with is the future volume of electric energy based on nuclear fission. Not the least of the reasons is that it has been so long on the horizon and so slow in materializing. This has led some to argue that the time of its appearance as a competitive force has finally arrived. Others say that we shall continue to chase a receding image for a good many years. At the moment, the optimists are in the ascendancy. They point to the fact that the margin between the cost of nuclear and conventionally generated electricity has been narrowing to the point where equipment manufacturers are offering nuclear equipment as reasonable alternatives to conventional facilities, and some of the largest utilities now have concrete plans for building large-scale plants. Finally, a nuclear reactor lends itself to incorporating subsequent improvements, so that while noncompetitive in its early years it will become ever more efficient and competitive over the lifetime of the plant. The conventional electric power plant, on the other hand, must remain pretty much as it is built.

A regional approach has again been followed in the case of nuclear energy, assuming that progressively lower costs can be achieved through technological improvements until nuclear-generated energy becomes competitive in one region after another. As soon as the competitive regional threshold has been reached, it is likely that most if not all subsequent major installations will be nuclear reactors, size considerations permitting.

By the end of the century, something like half of all electrical energy is projected as emanating from nuclear reactors. This estimate is undoubtedly hazardous—it is like looking into another world. There is the additional fact that by becoming more competitive the nuclear power industry will goad its conventional competitors into matching its cost reductions. Thus its very success will make it harder for nuclear energy to gain a larger share of the market. Despite all reservations, it seems likely that after a slow start, there will be a sudden acceleration, and a wholesale switch to nuclear generation of electricity—not throughout the country, but certainly in a great many localities.

The role of hydroelectric power has never been large in the United States. At present it contributes only 4 per cent of all energy. In the future it is likely to contribute even less. Thus the total hydroelectric potential that may be exploited in the next forty years is not too important in the national picture, although of utmost importance for a given locality or region. By the end of the century, known plans of development and estimates of theoretical potential add up to nearly three times as much hydroelectric capacity as there is now, with about three-fourths of the practical potential then being exploited. This would represent a substantial slowdown, for in 1960 the capacity was almost twice what it had been only ten years before. In the projected pattern, another doubling will not occur until 1980, and between 1980 and 2000 capacity will rise only by a little less than one-third. At some time in the late 1970's the generation of electricity by nuclear reactors should overtake that by hydro installations.

One would not want to exclude the possibility that during the balance of the century a way will be found to generate electricity through nuclear fusion rather than fission; or that the fuel cell will become a significant source of electricity. But costs, timing, and extent of use are at this time beyond the bounds of reasonable calculation.

When the separate analyses of the different aspects of energy use are brought together, one can form a general idea of the broad picture for the future. Figure 33 shows the current and projected sharing of the market among conventional fuels and nuclear and hydro power.

Chemical Uses of Energy Materials

Coal has for decades been a source of chemicals, as well as heat. Among the best-known chemicals are ammonium sulphate, a by-product of the steel industry's coke ovens and for a long time one of the principal sources of nitrogenous fertilizer, and the coal-tars that are turned into dyes, pharmaceuticals, and other end products. The postwar growth of the petroleum and natural gas industry has opened up a whole new source of hydrocarbon materials that has by now far overtaken the coal by-products. Coal may once again become an important source of chemical raw materials, but, for the time being, leadership has passed into the hands of the petroleum and gas industry—so much so that in popular usage the term petrochemicals includes even chemicals derived from coal. Indeed, when we speak of petrochemicals

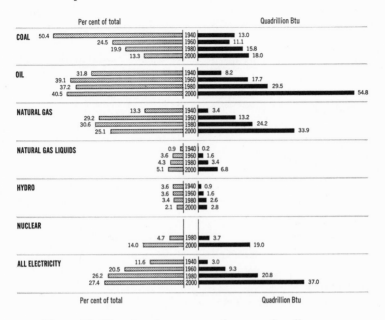

Figure 33. The changing pattern of sources for all energy.

today, we no longer think of by-products, but of a large, independent industry that, using mostly oil and natural gas as starting materials, produces a range of products stretching from man-made fibers and rubbers to soft or rigid plastics, drugs, paint, detergents, pesticides, fertilizers, etc. Figure 34 suggests the great variety of things made from a petroleum or gas base.

The advantages of the petrochemical product are obvious. It can be tailored to fit the intended use, whereas the natural substance has by and large to be taken as found. Petrochemicals can make a woodlike material without appeal to termites and with other advantageous features not possessed by wood; a fabric that moths won't eat and rain won't wet; a pipe that won't corrode and that weighs less than steel or even aluminum; a wrapping material that is light, transparent, and

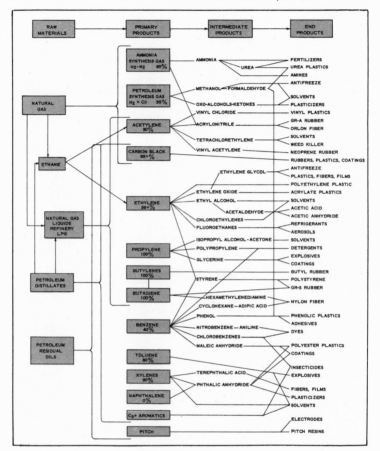

Figure 34. Petrochemicals and their uses.

waterproof, and has a tensile strength many times that of
paper. The fact that synthetics often cost more per pound,
yard, or unit of volume does not especially dampen their
competitive strength. Their use may lead to so many economies in processing and maintenance that the man-made
material can tolerate a higher price than its natural counterpart.

Statistics show that between 1950 and 1960 the use of gas- and oil-based hydrocarbons for chemical processing grew at the astounding rate of 15 per cent per year compounded. Such a rate means quadrupling every ten years. Not all underlying uses have grown, or will grow, at this rate. In the 1950's, for example, one of the older materials, phenolic resins (a plastic material much used in appliances, housewares, toys, etc.), rose by barely 50 per cent; while styrene resins, a close competitor and, like phenol, having benzene as a major starting material, tripled; and polyethylene use (for packaging, moldings, and other applications) rose some 25 times.

Despite these high rates of expansion the petrochemicals still form only a minute portion of the total demand for oil and gas—no more, and most likely less, than 2 per cent of the country's annual oil and gas consumption. But the steep growth of this industry, which as yet shows little sign of slackening, has made some people wonder whether in the more remote future petrochemicals may not become an important factor in determining the adequacy of oil and gas reserves in this country. Some even have gone so far as to call for a slowdown in the use of oil and gas as fuel in order to preserve them as chemical raw materials.

While it is obvious that the synthetics have a promising future, coming to grips with them statistically to test this is quite another matter. The chemical industry is most dynamic, with new products hitting the market rapidly and often disappearing just as quickly; its technology is exceedingly complex, and thousands upon thousands of end products emerge each year from its diverse, and generally secret, processes. The collection and dissemination of statistics reflect these difficulties.

The products that are of most interest under the aspect of resource adequacy—those derived from oil and natural gas—form the bulk of the synthetic organic chemicals obtained through conversion of coal, petroleum, gas, and to a minor extent a variety of plant materials such as fats, oils, grains, etc. It so happens that the U.S. Tariff Commission has for many years collected detailed data on production and shipments of many of these chemicals. For plastics and resin materials—the building blocks of so much of our everyday synthetic environment from unbreakable dishes to quick-drying wall paint—and the synthetic rubbers and fibers, one can hazard estimates of their future importance. In 1960, oil- and gas-derived material used in their production appears to have amounted to about 4½ million tons, out of a total of over 13 million tons of materials which the Tariff Commission says represent the "production and sales of crude products from petroleum and natural gas for chemical conversion." Tying the future growth of this total to a projection of the smaller sample of plastics, resins, rubbers, and fibers—on the generally reasonable hypothesis that this parcel of statistically calculable items is likely to become a smaller and smaller portion of the aggregate—one can derive a projection of this oil- and gas-derived total.

Table 6 shows the principal elements that have been projected as well as the total of which they form a part. A little over 50 million tons by 1980, and not quite 190 million tons by the end of the century is the result.

Equivalent in volume to 340 million and 1,230 million barrels of petroleum respectively, these quantities would amount to over 6 per cent of the total demand for crude oil in 1980 and 12 per cent in the year 2000. Thus, if derived only from crude oil, petrochemical demand would be a substantial factor in total oil demand by the end of the century. However, natural gas too is a starting material, and the demand for petrochemicals must be related, therefore, to oil and gas jointly. It then becomes apparent that even by the end of the century projected demand will be a significant, but by no means decisive factor in the total demand for oil and gas. This remains true even though only certain fractions of crude oil or natural gas are presently utilized as raw materials for the chemical industry, and the comparison of demand arising

Table 6. Use of Oil- and Gas-Derived Materials in Synthetics Manufacture

| | (*Billion pounds*) | | |
	1960	1980	2000
Organic crudes and intermediates in synthetics manufacture:			
Acetylene	0.64	2.23	4.81
Adipic Acid	.29	.82	1.38
Butadiene	1.92	4.55	7.50
Ethylene	1.31	4.82	11.32
Ethylene dichloride	.77	2.83	6.67
Formaldehyde	1.75	5.68	14.81
Phenol	.37	.97	2.34
Phthalic anhydride	.38	.75	1.63
Propylene	.15	3.08	11.88
Styrene	1.73	4.97	11.47
Total	9.31	30.70	73.81
All oil- and gas-derived material for manufacture of synthetic organic chemicals	26	102	369

from the chemical industry and total oil and gas use is therefore somewhat misleading. However, the portion that the chemical industry has been able to utilize has been growing, and the flexibility that the industry has developed in converting one type of hydrocarbon molecule into another does not make one pessimistic as to its future ability to derive many times the current relative fraction of petrochemicals from gas and oil. This type of flexibility is one that the chemical industry has exhibited in many of its activities, and that it will increasingly have to engage in as the demand for petrochemicals is growing at a much faster rate than the demand for all other gas and oil components. Thus, coping with the situation will call far more for developing new processes and products and making the necessary investment rather than escaping from any threatening raw material shortage.

4

Adequacy of Resources

In this chapter the projections of demand for resource products are compared with the magnitude of the natural resources from which they must be met to test the adequacy of available resources for sustaining continued economic growth in the United States. For the most part, discussion is limited to domestic resources that have been the traditional suppliers of most of the nation's needs, and are likely to remain so. In some instances, however, such as petroleum and some of the metals, it is necessary to consider foreign sources, which even now contribute part of this country's supply.

Inevitably, there are great uncertainties in looking ahead over a span of forty years that is bound to be marked by great technological advance and political change. These uncertainties are not confined to the demand side. Availability of a given resource in the amount required is not only a function of the physical environment, but also of the price that is offered for it. With the necessary effort (and therefore cost), cropland can be "created" where it does not exist. The addition of fertilizer and water will—at a cost—allow crops to be harvested on previously barren land. Similarly, mineral deposits will become attractive commercial ventures when the price of the metal, or metals, contained in the deposit is high enough to permit exploitation at a profit. In this way, reserves of ore are "created" just as fertile land is "created."

The degree of difficulty in defining the magnitude of resources varies among land, water, and the minerals, to name the three large conventional groupings of resources. Land, in this country at least, is reasonably well known in terms of area, quality of soil, topographic features, and other important characteristics. Uncertainty relates principally to the amount and kinds of economic activity that it can support in the future. If crops, what mix of crops? How much acreage to be devoted to trees, and how can the carrying capacity for trees be realistically determined? What areas for recreation, and what standards are there for judging the magnitude of land resources as carriers of resource activities?

In considering the outlook for fresh water, no change is anticipated in average annual precipitation during such a short span of time as forty years. The uncertainties relate, therefore, to the fraction of total precipitation that can be captured for use (which depends largely on the investment that the country is willing to make), to the technology that will be developed to maintain water quality at a desirable level, and to the progress in the art of adding to our fresh water supply through new techniques.

Uncertainties loom largest in the case of the minerals. First, our knowledge of the physical environment is still incomplete, and, as most deposits of most minerals lie below the surface, they become known only as efforts are made to find them. Second, there is insufficient information at hand to determine under what economic conditions it will or will not be profitable to exploit a given deposit. There are numerous factors, of which degree of concentration is only one, that make a deposit more or less valuable. When we talk of "reserves," we have in mind a deposit that can be mined profitably under current economic conditions and at current levels of technology. When we talk of "potential ore," we have in mind deposits that will become profitable at some future date, with progress in technology or higher prices, or a combination of the two. A more precise definition of conditions is rarely possible. Thus, judgment of adequacy must necessarily be rough.

Outside the United States the knowledge of geologic circumstances is often even less ample, and uncertainties of international trade and national politics aggravate the problem of availability. We have taken account of the latter problem to some extent by considering, with few exceptions, only the non-Communist world, both on the demand and the supply side. But in practice such a neat division, in which no supplies pass through the iron curtain, is not much more realistic than considering the resources and the demand of the entire world in one and the same calculation. If only the United States were involved, the matter would be less serious, since there has been in fact very little trade with Communist countries. But apart from the possibility that a flow of trade may develop between the United States and the U.S.S.R., Western Europe trades heavily with the Soviet Union and its satellites. So do members of the British Commonwealth. To the extent, therefore, that the United States depends on foreign supplies, or sells its products in foreign markets, it is affected by flows of trade abroad. Again, therefore, the resulting judgments necessarily have a wide margin of uncertainty.

WATER

In the preceding chapter we have worked out projected demand for every major natural resource material except water. The omission does not imply that water is any less important than the other resources or presents less significant problems. On the contrary, many of the uses of fresh water are key components in the nation's economy and, at least in small quantities, water is a necessity of life itself. In recent years questions of water supply have caused far deeper concern in some localities than has the outlook for any other resource. Discussion has been deferred for only one reason: demand and supply are so intermingled that it is much simpler to consider them together.

Some Definitions and Basic Concepts

Before examining the outlook for demand and then comparing it with the prospects for supply, let us look briefly at some unique characteristics of water use and water problems.

1. Almost all water situations and problems are local or regional, rather than nationwide. Because the cost of transporting large quantities of water over long distances is so high in relation to its value, there is no national market for water as there is for farm products, timber, metals and fuels, or even (because people will travel long distances to reach certain surroundings) for outdoor recreation. Generally speaking, a region's needs for fresh water have to be met from its own supplies; there can be a serious shortage in one part of the country while elsewhere large quantities are flowing unused to the sea. There are, it is true, a few large inter-basin diversion projects, but they are still the exception rather than the rule. For many purposes the river basin is the best unit of area to use in considering water situations. In this study, however, much larger units are used. This is because demand must be projected as well as the more easily calculated prospects of supply. The uncertainties of projecting population, patterns of industrial growth, and other elements of demand for particular areas are enormous; and the smaller the area, the greater the hazards. It has seemed best in this study to divide the country into only three regions—the well-watered East; the arid West; and the Pacific Northwest, most, but not all, of which is humid. The use of such very large areas inevitably blurs the analysis; some pockets of the humid East are quite dry, and some parts of the West are much drier than others. Nevertheless, separate consideration of the three regions can suggest the general outlook in each, whereas the national projections would conceal nearly all of the troublesome problems. But nationwide estimates are of interest in

making certain comparisons of trends in different kinds of water use and for that reason a few will be cited here.

2. Our projections apply only to the concentrated supplies of water gathered in surface watercourses and accessible underground aquifers that feed wells and to the demands made on these supplies. This leaves out the rain that falls on crops and grasslands and forests and is taken up and transpired by vegetation without ever entering the concentrated supply. Omission of this critically important (and by far the largest) use of fresh water in the United States may seem odd until one realizes that, failing far greater progress in rainmaking than seems likely in the next few decades, there is little that man can do to affect or manage it. Also we shall omit household water not supplied by municipal systems. Water pumped for all purposes from underground sources not replenished by rainfall has entered into the calculations for demand, but not for supply. Though these uses cause some important local problems, they involve many uncertainties and complexities and would not affect the over-all situations over large areas.

3. The uses of the concentrated supply of fresh water are extremely diverse. They are hard to compare, and some cannot even be estimated with any confidence under present techniques. The *withdrawal* uses, in which the water is actually taken out of streams, lakes, or wells, are the only ones for which there are nationwide statistics and even these are imperfect and recent. The principal withdrawal uses are municipal (for city and town water supplies), industrial, and farm irrigation. Then there are the *flow* uses (such as turning the turbines of hydroelectric plants, providing the place for sport fishing or boating and canoeing, affording enough channel depth for inland navigation, and carrying away wastes) for which the water is not withdrawn, but must flow. Third, there are the *on-site* uses in which the water just has to stay where it is; the largest use of this kind is to maintain swamps where wildfowl live. Finally, there is what might be termed a negative use: the flood hazard, which in many areas must

be curbed by elaborate dams and levees. The requirements
for these varied kinds of use—when they can be estimated at
all—clearly cannot be added together. And yet, because they
all involve the same substance—fresh water—they affect each
other in many ways. If the swamps that provide wildlife
habitat were drained, evaporation would be greatly reduced
and there would be greater flow for other purposes downstream. A storage dam intended solely for flood control would
be managed differently from one designed only to maintain
supplies for withdrawal use, and differently still from a multiple-purpose dam designed for both purposes and others as
well, such as maintaining channel depth.

4. The same water can be used several times. In its descent
from the headwaters to the mouth of a river some of the
water withdrawn for irrigation and nearly all of that withdrawn for municipal and industrial use finds its way back
into the stream. Furthermore, water withdrawn by an industrial plant for cooling can be recirculated many times before
being returned. Consequently, total withdrawal use in a
watershed can be as large as or even much larger than total
flow without necessarily implying a water shortage. Much
depends, however, on the quality of the returned water.
Without proper treatment the effluent of some household and
industrial uses is grossly contaminated, and in many areas
unused irrigation water picks up excessive amounts of mineral
salts. Thus the usable supply of fresh water often has to be
measured in terms of quality as well as quantity. Because
dilution is an alternative to elaborate treatment of wastes, a
sufficient flow of clean water to flush out polluted reaches
of streams is an important water use.

Indicators of Demand

Every day the American people use almost 300 billion
gallons of fresh water in homes, factories, and steam-generat-
ing plants or on irrigated farmland. In addition to these withdrawal uses, other huge quantities are "used," for a variety

of flow or on-site purposes that range from waste-carrying to simply providing restful and beautiful scenery.

Among the withdrawal uses, estimated municipal use in 1960 was 14 billion gallons per day, or barely 5 per cent of the total. By contrast, irrigation used 40 per cent; industry, 25 per cent; and power generation, 30 per cent. But because the effect of a temporary shortage in cities or towns is immediately felt by large numbers of people, possible shortages of municipal supplies have attracted much more attention than the larger uses of water in industry and irrigation.

With more people, greater industrial activity, and more leisure time for outdoor recreation, it is clear that requirements for fresh water are going to increase mightily between now and the year 2000. The outlook for the withdrawal uses can be projected with about the same degree of confidence as could the requirements for other key resources and resource materials developed in the preceding chapter. The possible size of the other requirements for water can only be speculated upon in a most general way. It does seem safe to say, however, that some of them will be large. Needs for dilution flow, for instance, may in many areas of the East be several times as large as total depletion resulting from withdrawal use.

Estimating withdrawal depletions. Much of the water that is withdrawn for use is returned to the watercourse and is thus available for reuse farther downstream. The amounts *not* returned (withdrawal depletions) are most nearly the equivalent of consumption and are therefore the best measure of demand. In irrigation the losses are large, averaging around 60 per cent in the West and 90 per cent in the East and Pacific Northwest. They are caused almost entirely by transpiration from plants or by other kinds of evaporation. The losses of water withdrawn by industries and inland cities are far smaller and result mainly from evaporation and transpiration, although some water is incorporated into manufactured products. Another source of depletion is discharge of water under conditions that preclude reuse as fresh water. This occurs almost entirely in coastal areas where used water goes into the sea or tidal estuaries. In such places the total amounts withdrawn must be considered as lost. In terms of regional averages this type of depletion is minor for industry, but important for cities.

The choice of depletion as the measure of water consumption requires an assumption that all the returned water (except discharges into saline water) is usable. And so it is, but at a cost. The effluents of some domestic and industrial uses are so polluted that the costs of making them fit for reuse can be high. Later in this section we shall consider some of the situations and problems that result.

Americans use water lavishly around the house. On the average, each urban resident draws about 60 gallons of water per day for domestic use. This includes lawn watering, air cooling and laundering, as well as personal requirements for drinking, cooking, bathing, and washing. Of this, the physiological "requirement" is probably around a gallon a day, either drunk straight or incorporated with food, tea, or coffee. Another 26 gallons per person per day is supplied to commercial establishments like restaurants and offices. In addition, the average municipality withdraws about 25 gallons per person per day for community services such as street cleaning and fire fighting. Altogether, then, the average American municipality has become accustomed to a supply of over 110 gallons per day per resident.

This figure simply reflects current usage, geared in large degree to the prevailing price structure of water. It includes the amounts lost in leaky faucets and pipes; the consumption by flush toilets designed without much attention to economizing water, and other traditional rates of use which in most parts of the United States are based on a carefree impression that water is practically free, and the frequently mistaken premise that additional supplies cost less than would measures of economy.

The prospect of rising incomes seems incompatible with a decline in per capita use of water, no matter how wasteful present household practices may be. In making projections, therefore, it has been assumed that current levels of use per person will prevail in the future, and that tendencies to increase it, such as additional appliances, air conditioning, and swimming pools, will be offset by somewhat lower per capita use that may be brought about in urban areas through a trend back to apartments and other multifamily dwellings. Hence, depletion of water by municipal use is largely a function of population growth.

Water has many uses in industry. It becomes an ingredient of some products; it is used to cleanse materials, and to transport them within a plant; it is an agent in many chemical processes; and serves other purposes. But by far the largest proportion of the water withdrawn by industry is for cooling, and the evaporation that results from cooling is the major source of water depletion by manufacturing. Such losses account for more than 80 per cent of all water consumed in petroleum refining, chemicals, and nonferrous metals, about 70 per cent in the iron and steel industry, and 50 per cent in the food products industry.

Industry has various ways of getting around the use of fresh water: air cooling and use of brackish or sea water are among the most widely used substitutes. In many locations, petroleum refining is changing over to air cooling. How far other industries will follow one cannot tell. In making our projections it has been assumed that the proportion of water derived from salt or brackish sources—which represented about 20 per cent of total use in 1954—will not change in the next forty years and that water depletion per unit of output will not change materially, either. Then, by using projections of output in the various branches of industry, plus data on the current use of water in those industries, one can project depletion of fresh water withdrawn by industry for various points of time in the future. The results of such calculations, made separately for the three broad regions, are shown in Figure 35.

Thermal electric power plants withdraw more water than any other category of use except irrigation. The projected large increase in electric power generation suggests that by the end of the century thermal generation will lead all other withdrawal uses. Yet the average loss per gallon withdrawn is so small—about 0.6 per cent in 1954 and still steadily declining—that it will remain by far the smallest source of withdrawal depletion.

Where cool water is readily available in large quantities, it is usually economical for generating plants to use the water on a once-through basis. However, under some other circumstances it is more economical to run the water through cooling towers and reuse it. At present, less than one-fifth of the water withdrawn is recirculated. The deciding factor is the relative cost of water and of additional equipment.

While the decision is an important one for an individual plant, recirculation does not materially affect the amount of cooling water that is depleted. The governing factor is the amount of heat that has to be dissipated in the process of converting fuel combustion to electric energy. With equipment now in use, it is estimated that approximately three-quarters of a gallon of water, on the average, is evaporated to dissipate the surplus heat produced in the generation of one kilowatt-hour of electricity. This represents an improvement of about 20 per cent since 1954, as a result of increases in the thermal efficiency with which fuel is utilized in power generation. Further increases in this efficiency—referred to as the heat rate—are expected. Our projections assume that by the end of the century 0.4 gallons of cooling water will be evaporated per kilowatt-hour of electricity generated, not much more than half the quantity required today.

Revolutionary technological and scientific advances could drastically alter the future demand outlook. Conceivably, a

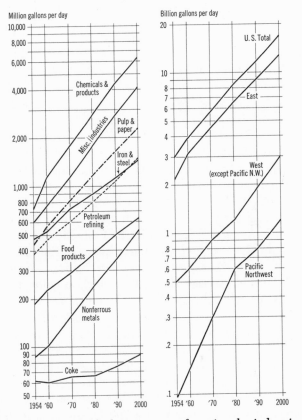

Figure 35. Fresh water depletion in manufacturing, by industries and regions.

type of air cooling that uses no water whatever might be substituted for conventional cooling processes. No allowance, however, has been made for such eventualities in our projections of water demand.

Irrigation accounts for about 40 per cent of all water withdrawals and more than 85 per cent of total withdrawal depletions.

Irrigation was practiced in certain parts of the West before

Columbus, and Spanish colonists brought water to additional small areas. But large-scale efforts really began with diversions from the Wasatch mountain streams in Utah in 1846. By 1949, more than 25 million acres were under full or partial irrigation. The rate of growth between 1954 and 1957—from over 27 million to 32 million acres—was one of the highest in U.S. history. This spurt was due in part to the development of drilling and pumping techniques to tap deep water-bearing sources. Large numbers of wells were sunk by individual landowners.

Irrigation is heavily concentrated in the arid and semiarid areas where it is essential to crop production. In 1960 about 80 per cent of the water withdrawn for irrigation use was in the West, 15 per cent in the Pacific Northwest (mostly in its drier sections), and 5 per cent in the East. Most of the irrigation in the East is supplementary; natural rainfall provides much of the needed moisture and extra water is used when drought would damage the crops, which usually are high-value, intensively cultivated vegetables and fruits.

In the West and Pacific Northwest, irrigation has been encouraged by federal policy and in most instances state policies as well. As a result, farmers pay less for diverted water than they otherwise would have to. Also, public policies are likely to continue to be an important factor influencing agricultural output. For these two reasons market forces will be only partially responsible for the extent of irrigation in the future. In making projections for the West and the Pacific Northwest, it has been assumed that, in addition to the 1957 acreage, private and public plans that the Commissioner of the Bureau of Reclamation in 1958 reported to be feasible and seriously contemplated will be completed by the year 2000. For the Eastern agricultural areas, where little public subsidy is involved, the projection is an extension on the trend in Eastern irrigated acreage between 1949 and 1957.

Considerations of cost and prices have entered into the estimates for both dry and humid regions. At different costs to the consumer, water will undoubtedly be applied with different degrees of care. Variations in prices to growers could significantly affect the "requirements" of agriculture for water.

In the East it has been assumed that by reason of improved practices the amount of water diverted per irrigated acre will drop from its 1960 level of more than 2.5 acre-feet per year to less than 2 acre-feet in 2000. The proportion of the withdrawn water that is depleted is expected to remain high— slightly over 90 per cent instead of slightly below that level, as in 1960. This change would be a result of increased efficiency; more of the water applied to the crops would actually be used by the crops and disappear through transpiration. At present, only about 60 per cent of irrigation withdrawals are depleted in the West; a gradual increase to something like 65 per cent by the end of the century is assumed. This would represent a gain in efficiency: less water lost through breaks in irrigation ditches; more actually brought to plants and then transpired.

At the end of the century irrigation still is expected to be the largest cause of water depletion in each of the three regions. Although absolute withdrawal losses would increase, irrigation's share of depletion from all causes would decline somewhat. For the nation as a whole, about 75 per cent of withdrawal depletions in the year 2000 would be attributable to irrigation, instead of over 85 per cent in 1960. Figure 36 shows the current and projected depletion from withdrawal uses in the different regions and in the different uses.

Flow and on-site uses. Although the nonwithdrawal uses of water are large and important, as yet there is no satisfactory way of measuring them statistically on a uniform basis or, in some instances, on any basis at all. Of great promise, however, is the work done for the Senate Select Committee in 1960 when, in a study directed by Nathaniel Wollman, a framework was devised for expressing all requirements in terms of flow in billions of gallons per day. To the quantities

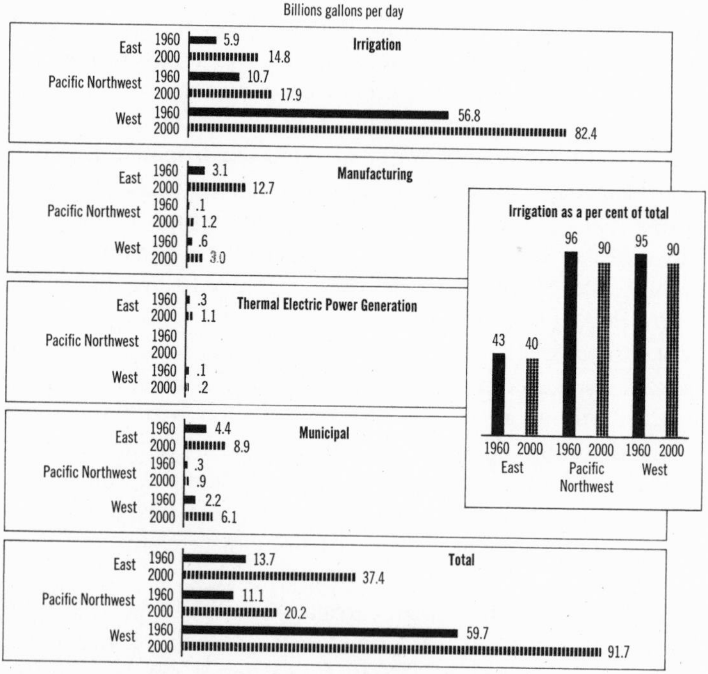

Figure 36. Fresh water depletion by all uses: variations among three regions.

required for each of the uses—hydroelectric generation, maintaining sufficiently deep navigation channels, etc.—are added the amounts lost to flow through withdrawal depletions or the evaporation of surface water in wetlands or water held on farmland by terraces or other conservation structures. The flow requirements, of course, cannot be added together. The same water that turns hydroelectric turbines can also maintain channel depths and provide habitat for fish. If water for the largest flow requirement in a region is available, it can be presumed that the other flow requirements can be met. The Select Committee made projections of the different kinds of requirements, but, as the Committee pointed out, they were necessarily tentative, based on fragmentary data and untested assumptions. Also, some of the assumptions are very different from those used in this study, and tend in general to result in higher projections of demand.

We cannot, therefore, in this study treat the Select Committee's estimates of on-site and flow requirements as comparable to our own projections of withdrawal depletions. It does seem clear, though, that largely because of pollution, flow requirements in many parts of the country will be considerably larger than withdrawal depletions, and that except in the Pacific Northwest on-site losses may be half or more as large as the withdrawal losses.

Requirements to maintain water quality. The best guide to flow requirements is the quantity of fresh water needed to keep watercourses reasonably clean. It is generally true that if there is enough flow to satisfy the requirements for waste carriage, there will also be enough to satisfy the remaining flow uses, especially in the East. Moreover, navigation and hydroelectric uses are of relatively low economic value: there are other ways of generating power and providing transport.

Many kinds of pollutants get into watercourses and affect the usefulness of supply—sediment from soil erosion, agricultural pesticides washed off fields, chlorides for ice control washed off highways, salts dissolved in a stream bed or leached from the soil by irrigation water, organic wastes from households and both organic and inorganic compounds from manufacturing. Steam electric and manufacturing plants return water to streams warmer than when it was withdrawn—such heat pollution can have far-reaching effects on the quality of water.

Some of the results of pollution, like salinity from irrigation, are limited to certain river basins. Others, like certain types of chemical pollution, still are little understood technologically. Few can be systematically projected. The exception—a large one—is the problem of organic wastes from homes and industries. Dilution of organic wastes constitutes a large potential claimant for fresh water, as urban population continues to grow and industrial activity to expand.

Complex relationships are involved in estimating the demand upon a given supply of water for organic waste disposal. The capacity of the receiving water to absorb wastes is determined by such factors as volume of streamflow, rate of flow, temperature, and chemical content. Another significant variable is the extent to which organic wastes have been removed by treatment prior to discharge.

The basic measure of organic pollution is known as biochemical oxygen demand (BOD). This indicates the rate at which dissolved oxygen is drawn upon in a waste-receiving water. The rate of BOD, combined with the rate at which oxygen is restored, determines the level of dissolved oxygen in the water. If the oxygen level drops very low, fish are killed; other, usually undesirable, changes occur, and, ultimately, septic conditions arise. Unassimilated organic wastes may also add to the difficulty and expense of treating withdrawals for municipal and industrial purposes.

In flowing water there is first a fall and then a rise in dissolved oxygen as wastes are carried downstream. The degradation of wastes, together with the restoration of dissolved oxygen under natural conditions, is often termed "self-purification." Through speeding up and controlling the processes which naturally occur in a stream, biological treatment plants can reduce waste loads and take some of the burden off the streams, lakes, and estuaries into which wastes are discharged. Industrial processes themselves also can often be adjusted so as to reduce the volume or concentration of harmful wastes.

While receiving waters are capable of recovering from the oxygen demand imposed by organic waste loads, other effects may follow the biological degradation of organic waste. The residual products of organic waste degradation are plant nutrients (nitrogen, phosphorus, carbon) which may foster algae growth. Since algae produce organic matter by means of photosynthesis, they periodically release oxygen, but when they die they become organic material which exerts an oxygen demand. Thus they are involved in the oxygen balance of the receiving water. In addition, when algae occur in great quantities, they affect the appearance, the taste, and the odor of the water.

The desired oxygen content of the water can be achieved by prior treatment of the waste, by augmenting the flow of water, or by a combination of methods. For example, treated effluents can be held in lagoons, algae growth can be fostered, and the algae harvested to remove the plant nutrients and break the vicious cycle. Effluents can be discharged into a separate channel emptying into the ocean without polluting the natural stream. Wastes can be held in lagoons, then discharged when flows are high—although for large cities and big plants this may not be practicable because of the space required. Waste water can, of course, be purified by distillation but present processes for doing this are too costly for use on a large scale.

Over large areas with differing conditions, one can achieve only a rough approximation of a low-cost, efficient program for maintaining water quality. There is still much to be learned, for example, about the oxygen standard that should be maintained in waste-receiving water. Even when a quality standard has been agreed on, it is difficult to assess the demand for water quality maintenance: market forces cannot function effectively to establish a demand, and the political process is only now becoming sensitive to the question. With allowance for all these uncertainties, regulation of streamflow to provide more water during periods of low flow is generally looked upon at present as the least costly means of supplementing traditional treatment measures in most areas. With the growing interest in new methods of intensive treatment, however, progress in less conventional alternatives to storage can be expected.

All water uses together. Demands on the nation's fresh water resources will multiply between 1960 and 2000. Net losses of water resulting from the withdrawal uses will nearly double by the year 2000. Irrigation will continue to be the largest single cause of water depletion. Municipal and industrial withdrawal, however, will represent steadily increasing shares of total losses. The need for increased streamflow to dilute organic wastes is for all practical purposes a large new use. In most areas, dilution flow requirements will determine the combined requirements for flow, though in some places other flow needs will augment the total. In addition, there will be on-site requirements that cannot for the purposes of this study be projected numerically.

Part of the increase in demand for fresh water will come about simply from population growth, stepped-up industrial activity, and the boom in outdoor recreation in which fresh, clean water is an element. This general trend will be reinforced, however, by continued urbanization, especially as a source of domestic and industrial pollution.

Characteristics of Supply

Fresh water is the renewable resource *par excellence.* Through the hydrologic cycle, which might be termed nature's own desalinization process, pure water vapor is absorbed by the air from the oceans and is later precipitated as rain or snow. The precipitation that falls inland either flows to the sea or is returned directly to the atmosphere through evaporation or transpiration. Of the two current lines of effort to increase fresh water supplies, weather modification is an attempt to alter the hydrologic cycle so as to make rain fall where it is most needed, and desalinization seeks to supplement the cycle by getting fresh water from salt water by more direct means. In both instances the sea is the ultimate source.

Although in the course of the cycle large quantities of fresh water are stored in underground aquifers or surface lakes, it is annual precipitation that sets the ceiling on a region's water supply over any considerable period. Other stored water is for all practical purposes unconnected to the water cycle. Accumulated over geologic time in various ways, it lies at such great depths that it is not available to satisfy the demands with which we are concerned here. Since the supply is replenished so slowly, withdrawal is akin to mining. Because exploitation of the water stored in deep aquifers is costly in most areas, and such sources are not renewable, only the water in the hydrologic cycle will be considered here.

On the average, but with wide variations among areas, approximately 30 inches of rain fall each year over the forty-eight contiguous states. Of this, about 70 per cent never becomes a concentrated supply in a stream, lake, or aquifer, but is evaporated or transpired by vegetation to the atmosphere. The remainder, called runoff, totals about 1,100 billion gallons a day, and constitutes the potentially available concentrated supply.

There are great differences in timing as well as location. In addition to the fairly regular seasonable variations in precipitation there are irregular variations: dry years, very dry years, wet years, very wet years. For example, while the average flow of the Colorado River at Lee's Ferry is 13.2 million acre-feet per year, annual flows of almost twice and less than half of that level have been recorded. Then in many areas there are tremendous short-term variations. To use Lee's Ferry again as an example, a peak flow of 220,000 cubic feet per second and a low flow of only 750 have been recorded. The average is about 18,000.

Smoothing out these variations is one of the chief aims of water management. Storage in natural lakes, artificially constructed surface reservoirs, and underground aquifers may carry runoff from periods of large supply through periods of dryness. Storage dams have generally been considered as the best means of compensating for natural variations in streamflow. But adjustment of demand to variations in flow and the use of underground storage certainly warrant greater consideration than they have received in the past. There comes a point beyond which increasing storage capacity is not economically justified, partly because surface storage entails losses by evaporation, especially in hot, dry areas. The chief reason, however, is that the building of storage dams becomes progressively less effective in leveling out flow.

In any region significant measures of water supply, therefore, are:

1. Average runoff.

2. Maximum dependable flow: that is, the largest flow that could be made available 100 per cent of the time by providing more storage, regardless of cost. Such a flow would equal total runoff minus the evaporation that would occur in the storage dams.

3. Flow available 95 per cent of the time with the storage facilities that were available in 1954, which is the last time a complete survey was made. The additional storage that would be needed to make this level of flow available all the time would in most areas require an easily attainable further investment.

4. Flow available 50 per cent of the time with 1954 storage facilities. Although the investments necessary to maintain this level all of the time in most areas would still be large, they would be far smaller than those required to develop maximum dependable flow.

Adequacy of Supplies: The Outlook by Region

When the projected withdrawal depletions, together with a rough idea of flow and on-site requirements, are compared with the various levels of water availability, one gets a general picture of the outlook for each of the three great regions of the United States, and of the nature and scale of efforts that may be required to assure continuing adequacy of water supply.

The East. The relatively high runoff over the land area of the Eastern United States, which averages about 14.7 inches per year, accounts for over 70 per cent of the average volume of runoff of the forty-eight contiguous states. Precipitation is reasonably well distributed throughout the year, so that crops can be cultivated without irrigation, or in some instances with only auxiliary irrigation. Nevertheless, there are periods of low runoff, and at times there are droughts which have created demand for augmenting dependable supplies.

In the East the amounts of water withdrawn and consumed, and thus not put back into the water source, are extremely small in comparison with the maximum dependable flow (see Figure 37). By the year 2000, projected depletion would amount to less than 5 per cent of the maximum flow. It would represent less than half of the flow available 95 per cent of the time with storage facilities as reported in the 1954 survey. And even this favorable situation could be improved by the year 2000, either through the provision of additional storage or through instituting economies in the use of water.

It would probably take an increase of storage of about 20 per cent above present facilities to make the 95-per-cent-of-the time flow available at *all* times; or if the public at the end of the century is willing to cut down 5 per cent on water use for short periods, no increase in storage would be needed.

In either event, meeting withdrawal depletion in the East presents no large-scale problem. The same is true for the quantities projected for on-site use. But needs for waste dilution flow could radically change the outlook. If one were to accept at face value the projections for waste dilution flow uses (and for the relatively small requirements of on-site use) made a few years ago by the Senate Select Committee on National Water Resources, and add to these the RFF projections of withdrawal depletion, the resulting total use by 1980 would be 311 billion gallons per day. This would

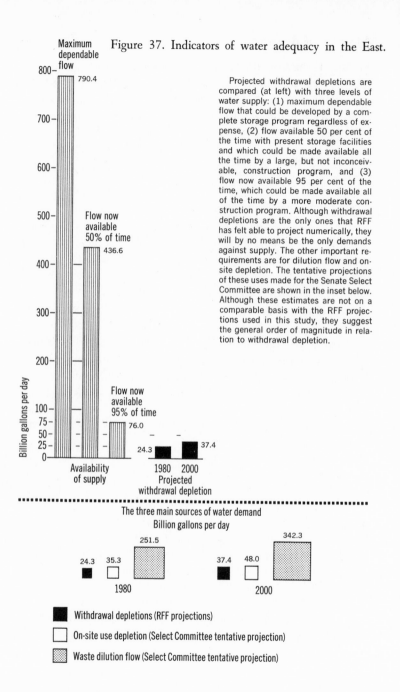

Figure 37. Indicators of water adequacy in the East.

Projected withdrawal depletions are compared (at left) with three levels of water supply: (1) maximum dependable flow that could be developed by a complete storage program regardless of expense, (2) flow available 50 per cent of the time with present storage facilities and which could be made available all the time by a large, but not inconceivable, construction program, and (3) flow now available 95 per cent of the time, which could be made available all of the time by a more moderate construction program. Although withdrawal depletions are the only ones that RFF has felt able to project numerically, they will by no means be the only demands against supply. The other important requirements are for dilution flow and on-site depletion. The tentative projections of these uses made for the Senate Select Committee are shown in the inset below. Although these estimates are not on a comparable basis with the RFF projections used in this study, they suggest the general order of magnitude in relation to withdrawal depletion.

The three main sources of water demand
Billion gallons per day

■ Withdrawal depletions (RFF projections)

□ On-site use depletion (Select Committee tentative projection)

▨ Waste dilution flow (Select Committee tentative projection) amount to almost 40 per cent of the maximum dependable flow—or about four times the daily flow of 76 billion gallons now available 95 per cent of the time.

If requirements of these dimensions had to be met by increased flow alone, large additional storage facilities would have to be provided. By 1980 the storage facilities of 1954 would have to be tripled by the addition of nearly 200 million acre-feet of storage. By the year 2000, around 300 million acre-feet of storage beyond that existing in 1954 would be needed to assure dependable flow. There are, however, two other ways out: (1) pollution abatement methods that use less water, including changes in industrial processes and more extensive treatment of wastes, and (2) allowing the stipulated standards of water quality to go unmet part of the time.

The alternatives suggest several significant questions. What water quality standards will the nation strive to maintain? In terms of dollars, it is probably cheaper to permit many reaches of streams periodically to fall below the level of cleanliness that these calculations imply. This is the practice in parts of Europe, and with proper precautions it need not be a menace to health. However, the explosive demand for outdoor recreation in the United States suggests that there will be considerable pressure to maintain clean water supplies at all times.

Another question raised is that of technology and new management techniques, especially the extent to which waste treatment can economically substitute for dilution flows. For example, if plant nutrients could be removed from the effluent of sewage treatment plants by less costly processes than those now known, such treatment could be economically substituted for dilution flows in many cases. Similarly, if arrangements could be made to store some wastes during low-flow periods and release them during high flows, less dilution water would be needed.

The West. Most of this region is arid or semiarid. The West includes more than half of the land surface of the forty-eight contiguous states but its average runoff of only about 2.3 inches per year accounts for less than 16 per cent of the country's average runoff. The bulk of the runoff originates at high elevations from snow melts. Because of the deficiency of water, a relatively high degree of regulation through storage reservoirs is already provided.

The water problems of the West differ from those of the East in both kind and degree (see Figure 38). A major proportion of its water supply, which is only about one-fifth of that in the East, is currently used for irrigation. As a result, estimated total withdrawal depletion in 1960 in the West was more than four times what it was in the East.

If by the year 2000 enough storage capacity could be built

Figure 38. Indicators of water adequacy in the West.

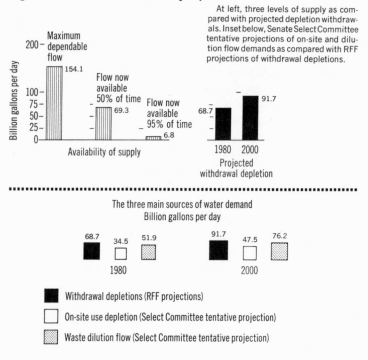

At left, three levels of supply as compared with projected depletion withdrawals. Inset below, Senate Select Committee tentative projections of on-site and dilution flow demands as compared with RFF projections of withdrawal depletions.

to develop maximum dependable flow, withdrawal depletion of water would claim 60 per cent of that supply (leaving waste dilution and on-site needs still to be provided for). To provide a dependable flow sufficient to meet just the projected withdrawal losses would probably require some 100 million acre-feet added to storage existing in 1954. Sharply rising costs would doubtless be encountered, because each successive unit of storage does less to level out flow during the year, and because the already highly-developed storage facilities have pre-empted most of the best natural dam sites.

Furthermore, water supply is most unequally distributed throughout the subregions of the West. About 60 per cent of the total occurs in the Western Gulf and the Central Pacific basins, leaving a relatively small amount for the other areas. The stringency is most serious in the upper Rio Grande and the Pecos basins, the Great Basin, the Colorado River Basin, and the Southern Pacific Basin. Over this area, supplies allocated to various uses under state laws already exceed maximum dependable flows. But even when one takes into account the more favorable supply situation in the Western Gulf and the Central Pacific basins in a single projection of the outlook for the West as a whole, the prospects still are disturbing: if the demands for flow and on-site uses projected in the Senate Select Committee report were to be borne out, regional demands would slightly exceed total supplies by 1980. By 2000, demand would exceed estimated maximum supply by 40 per cent. Even if the Committee estimates are too high, the West, particularly in its Rocky Mountain and Southwest regions, clearly faces a difficult problem.

One possibility for easing the situation is diversion of supplies from water-surplus to water-deficient areas (work has actually begun on at least one scheme—to divert water from the Central Pacific to the Southern Pacific Basin). Among the problems of diversion are high cost, which would exclude the use of such water for irrigation, and the opposition from residents of those areas from which the supplies would be

diverted. Distances involved and differences in elevation seem
to bar diversion from the Western Gulf Basin, rich in water,
to other areas of the West.

It is too soon to predict the practicality of new techniques
for increasing supplies of fresh water. Without considerable
scientific advance, possible gains from weather modification
seem small. The atmospheric conditions have to be just right
to stimulate precipitation, and the location of the precipitation cannot be predicted with accuracy. Furthermore, weather
modification may mean a change in the location of precipitation rather than a net addition to the total for a large region.
Although desalinization of salty or brackish water is already
in use in some parts of the world, it is still too costly at most
locations to be economically justified. Pilot plants built or
under construction by the federal government provide fresh
water from the ocean at a cost of $1.00 or more per thousand
gallons. Improvements of technology that now can be foreseen
may reduce costs to as little as 40 or 50 cents a thousand gallons. It is doubtful whether in most agricultural enterprises
a cost above 5 cents per thousand gallons could be tolerated
for any length of time. Hence, either a major technological
breakthrough or long-sustained improvement in currently
known processes is needed to change the outlook materially.

Much could be gained by reducing losses from evaporation.
In Western reservoirs these losses average around 19 billion
gallons per day, a larger quantity than is withdrawn annually
for municipal uses in the entire United States. One possible
remedy is greater use of underground storage. Another is
covering reservoirs with a chemical film. Experiments indicate
favorable results while the layer lasts, but making it withstand the action of wind and other disturbances is still a major
problem.

Water can, of course, be used with greater efficiency.
Evaporative type coolers used for air conditioning could be
replaced by the refrigeration type. Conventional lawns and
shrubbery in homes and yards could be replaced by desert

grasses and shrubs. Saline water could take the place of fresh water in some industrial applications, particularly cooling. Or in some processes water cooling might be replaced by air cooling; to some extent this is already being done in petroleum refining. However, the major opportunity in the West for reducing depletion and using water more efficiently lies in agriculture, the heaviest user. The elimination of nonbeneficial vegetation along canals, reduction of losses in transit, and selected application of proper quantities of water at the proper time would also minimize water use, as would restriction of water supplies to the most productive land.

Making such methods work requires more than mere knowledge that they exist. Many farmers do not know how to apply practicable water-saving techniques. Beyond this, some students of the problem believe that Western water law and water pricing policies fail to encourage efficient water use, and may actually militate against it.

Major adjustments in the pattern of water use—particularly in the Southwest—will be essential if the arid West is to share fully in the nation's economic growth. In the driest parts of the region, municipal and industrial use can support a far larger amount of economic activity per unit of water depletion than does agriculture—perhaps at a ratio of 50 or 60 to 1. A transfer to municipal and industrial use of 10 per cent of the irrigation depletion projected for the year 2000 would support nearly double the projected level of depletion from municipal and industrial activity. The results in economic growth could be very substantial, with plenty of water remaining for specialty crops, such as citrus fruit.

The Pacific Northwest. The coastal portion of this region is humid, but east of the Cascade Mountains the climate is arid or semiarid. Much of the runoff comes from snow melt in the mountains. Compared with the West, however, runoff is high, averaging nearly 12 inches per year.

The Pacific Northwest, like the East, has a large supply of water in comparison with existing and prospective depletion (see Figure 39). Even if tentative estimates of on-site uses and waste dilution flows are added to projected depletion, the total would still be not much over one-third of maximum available flows. Already-planned future storage, primarily for hydroelectric power generation and flood control, promises dependable flows in much of the region that will be more than adequate to meet prospective demand.

On the other hand, the area east of the Cascades faces problems similar to those in the West. On some tributaries, available supplies are almost all developed. In other instances, the development of additional supplies for irrigation is of

Figure 39. Indicators of water adequacy in the Pacific Northwest.

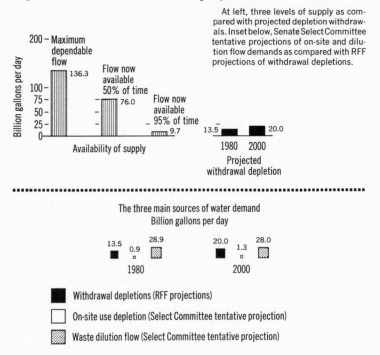

dubious merit because of high costs. Here again the problem is one of moving toward a pattern and level of economic activity consistent with the availability and cost of water. Plenty of water is available to support a substantial growth of cities and industry, if other location factors are favorable.

In Conclusion: The Nation As a Whole

The water outlook in the United States gives cause for neither alarm nor complacency. Although for the most part each area must meet its own needs from its own supplies, the national prospects are also significant because within the country people can move where the water supplies are, or can be developed. Thanks to the mobility of individuals and industries, the nation's natural endowment of fresh water is more than adequate to support continued economic growth throughout the twentieth century and beyond.

But some of the local and regional problems are formidable. In some areas, mostly in the West, demands will press hard upon total supplies, or outrun them. Much more widespread will be problems of water quality even in areas where total supplies are ample. In both instances the toughest issues are likely to be institutional and economic rather than technological. Even though much is yet to be learned through research, much is known already about how to build dams, design waste treatment plants, and water-saving industrial processes.

The hardest problems of limited supply may well be what to do about the impact of regional adjustments and costs upon families, communities, and industries. If it seems best for an area as a whole to shift some water from agriculture to other uses, what about the families who would have to leave farms, and what about the small towns whose main function has been to service irrigated farm country?

In maintaining water quality, the fundamental problem grows out of the prospect of a quadrupling of gross national product, a near doubling of population, and the consequent potential demand for use of streams as waste disposers: In view of this, how clean and sightly should watercourses be kept?

Then there are more specific questions of how to achieve quality standards: What combination of new storage reservoirs, waste treatment, and new industrial processes to save water will be most advantageous for a given area? Some of the stickiest problems of industrial pollution will be those of who pays for what: Should industrial users be given incentives for reducing waste loads, or be assessed on the basis of their wastes, or be required by law to measure up to prescribed standards?

Among the questions that will come up when new storage seems to be called for are those of where to put the dam. The extent to which reservoirs should be permitted in the name of economic efficiency to encroach upon scenic areas already is warmly controversial in many areas. Sometimes the issue is whether to flood productive agricultural land.

These and many other basic questions that bear on water supply and demand will be substantially affected by political as well as economic processes. Knowing more about the economic issues involved will lead to a better understanding of the costs of the many alternatives and of their impact upon different segments of the economy.

LAND

Land furnishes food, fibers, lumber, and other products of farms, grassland, and forests. It is the space on which we erect towns and cities, build highways, run railroads, and construct airports. Outdoor recreation, wildlife habitat, reservoirs, and other aspects of water management—all involve the use of land surfaces.

Not counting Alaska and Hawaii, the land surface of the United States amounts to roughly 1,900 million acres. But acreage alone tells us little about the capacity of the land to support 330 million or more people by the end of the century.

Differences in climate, topography, and soil affect the land's capacity to provide goods and services. The hours of light and sunshine are fixed, and it appears that little can be done so far to change the basic temperature pattern. But earth-moving machinery can alter the topography; chemicals can modify soil properties; reclamation, drainage, and irrigation can affect the conditions of humidity; river regulation or road construction can alter the map. Thus, within limits, land characteristics can be changed.

Roughly two-thirds of all land has in the past been devoted to agriculture and grazing, and around one-quarter to forestry. The balance has gone to all other uses: cities, parks, highways, and just nature. This means that nine out of every ten acres of land in the United States are used for growing crops to be consumed directly, to be fed to livestock, or to be turned into fiber and forest products.

Today's land use pattern is not the result of systematic planning. Not all the best soil is in crops, and some poor soil is farmed. Towns and cities occupy good farming land; crops are grown on millions of acres of land that is better suited to grazing or some nonagricultural use. On the whole, however, clashes between land capability and land use are gratifyingly small.

Without most of us realizing it, we have gone through a successful agricultural revolution since World War II. The question before us as we face the future is: At what levels of population and income growth are strains likely to appear in today's pattern of land use? Can the same area that provided the highest standard of living in the world for 180 million Americans in 1960 support 330 million or more in the year 2000 with a still higher standard of living?

Past successes not only in meeting our own needs but in helping a hungry world seem to furnish a quick answer. After all, we produce so much that we have to figure out ways of giving it away. But if one thinks a moment, it becomes clear that land space to support almost twice today's population is going to have to be found somewhere. Even if we should soon be able to rely entirely on man-made fibers, land will remain the key resource, for the day of man-made foods is still far away.

Cropland

The amount of land needed for crops is determined by its productivity. Land ranges widely, from the ideal acre through the barely marginal to the completely useless. An acre of cropland that one year lies fallow and the next year grows wheat by dry farming is physically but not economically the same acre once water has been brought in allowing it to be cropped every year. An acre newly drained, permitting its use in a wet spring, constitutes just as real an increase in acreage as a brand new acre of land physically added to the old supply. The addition of enough fertilizer to double the productivity of an acre effectively increases by one acre the total land base on which agriculture rests.

The growth in agriculturally useful acreage brought about by human effort is one result of the technological revolution in agriculture. The physical acreage from which crops were harvested in 1960 was not much different from that of a half century earlier. But the average acre in 1960 yielded some two-thirds more in crops—thus saving us the necessity for finding 250 million acres of additional farming land. Just about the entire area of the European Common Market—farms, towns, and cities—could be fitted into the acreage that has been "added" to the United States in this way in the last fifty years.

Additional acreage is created not only by higher yields, but by replacing work animals with machinery. Since 1920 some 80 million acres have been freed for growing crops other than horse and mule feed—more than enough to accommodate a country the size of Norway or the Philippines. Figure 40

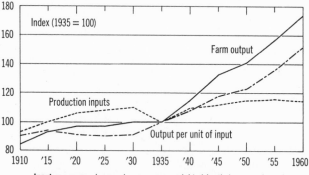

Input measures changes in resources, weighted by their respective prices, that flow into farm production. They include labor, real estate (annual interest, depreciation, repair, etc.), power and machinery (annual charges, fuel, etc.), fertilizer and other chemicals, taxes, financial charges, etc.

Output measures changes in the annual aggregate of products for human use, weighted by their respective prices. Feed crops and hay fed to livestock are excluded, and other minor adjustments are made to avoid double-counting.

Figure 40. Rising productivity in agriculture: farm output and production inputs.

suggests the sweep of the agricultural revolution by comparing input of all factors of production with farm output.

The trend toward higher productivity is by no means a one-way street. Agricultural land of high quality in a particular location may be of much greater value for uses other than farming, so that buyers bid it out of agricultural use. The immediate effect is a drop in the efficiency of the average agricultural acre. As high quality land is replaced by land of lower quality, capital must be invested to make the replacement equally productive. These losses—their extent is unknown—must be balanced off against the gains cited above.

While land was abundant and cheap it was easy to satisfy the requirements of a growing population by increasing the acreage of land under cultivation. Nowadays, we look to increases in productivity. Figure 41 shows percentage increases in yield for a number of crops over a 35-year period.

Cotton illustrates how this process has worked (see Figure 42). Production of cotton increased almost exclusively through

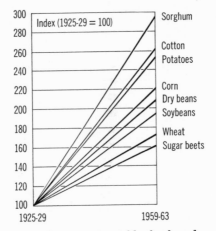

Figure 41. Increases in yield of selected crops.

expansion in acreage until the late 1920's. After that point, acreage declined, while yield rose steadily with only brief interruptions. This has turned out to be something of a sequence in American agriculture: expansion of acreage followed by expansion of yield per acre. To the end of the century, increased yield will remain the major factor in rising production.

There is no single cause for the great upsurge in yield per acre. Some of the improvement came from relocation of producing acres—the shift of cotton growing to California is an example. More acreage under irrigation, more acreage per farm, and mechanization are among other factors.

Mechanization and plant improvement are often interrelated. As the farm on which a given crop is grown increases in size, mechanized farming becomes more feasible, sometimes imperative. This in turn may lead to developing new plant strains better suited to mechanical farming. Breeding small grains for stiffer straws, tomatoes for tougher skins, cotton for simultaneous maturing, corn for ears that will not droop are examples.

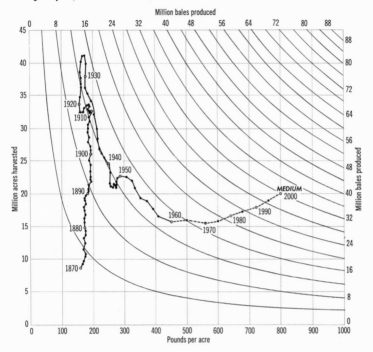

Figure 42. The interplay of acreage and yield in cotton output: the past record and future projections. Points on line showing production are based on a nine-year moving average.

Modern methods of deliberate and systematic crossing of plants, guided by a knowledge of genetics, have achieved striking results. Increased yields, lessened vulnerability to natural hazards, greater ability to withstand drought, heightened resistance to insects, disease, and wind damage, adaptability of different varieties to different climatic conditions—all these characteristics and more have been successfully bred into new strains. Hybrid corn is a spectacular example. Parallel developments in the livestock field are artificial insemination and selected breeding.

While the effect of fertilizer is vast, its use in this country is still surprisingly moderate. In recent years, only about half the acreage of inter-tilled crops, such as corn and cotton, and little more than one-quarter of the close-growing crops, such as small grains, were fertilized. Even so, the use of chemical fertilizer in 1960 was about six times the level of the 1930's. The additional production flowing from the recent rate of consumption of some 6 to 7 million tons of plant nutrients per year, at the current rates of application, is roughly equivalent to the yield from some 75 million acres of unfertilized farmland. Substantial future gains are still possible, not only through improved chemicals and better methods of applying them, but through improved cultivation practices.

The first real boost in crop yields in forty years occurred during World War II. A second even steeper rise took place in the 1950's. Recent years have been marked by sustained high yields of the level first reached around 1958 for most crops.

Are recent increases in yields mere spurts, or part of a continuous trend? While judgment varies from crop to crop, there can be little doubt that for the major U.S. crops, bigger yields lie ahead. The results achieved under controlled experiment conditions, the gaps in performance between the top producers and the average, as well as the large reservoir of little exploited knowledge at the disposal of farming, all point in that direction.

Livestock feed.   In estimating acreages required to grow food and fiber crops, one need not go beyond the simple operation of dividing total requirements for wheat, sugar, cotton, etc., by the projected yield per acre. But to estimate the amount of land that must be devoted to the raising of livestock for production of meat, milk, eggs, etc., requires a good many intermediate steps.

First, the total demand for livestock products must be broken down, for it is important to know the kinds of animals,

how they are fed, and what they are fed for. The yield per
unit of feed consumed differs among animals in absolute
amount, and each animal's diet is different. Some take more
roughage, which includes hay, pasture, and other bulky feeds,
and some take more concentrates, which include grains and
oilseed meals and other by-products. Cattle can live on roughage only, if need be. Hogs and chickens depend overwhelm-
ingly on concentrates. As a result, the future pattern of food
consumption has a lot to do with the future pattern of feed
consumption, and, therefore, with the demand for land.

Second, there is much flexibility in the feed mix of each
class of livestock. Whether they are grazed more, and on what
kind of land—cropland, open pasture, range—whether they
are fed more or less corn, or sorghum, or small grains like
oats or wheat (when the price is right), or whether the
proportion of by-products such as oilcake is kept high or low,
all this affects the demand for cropland and for the different
types of rangeland. Principal trends assumed here include a
continuing moderate rise in per capita beef consumption as
compared with pork; a slight improvement in the efficiency
with which feed is converted into livestock products; and a
small relative shift in the feed mix from roughage to concentrates, principally for cattle and calves and milk cows. It is
also assumed that hay consumption will rise at the expense
of pasturing; and that cropland pasture would be required
only to the extent that other forms of grazing which demand
less valuable land could not meet the demand for roughage
other than hay. Since the farmer has several alternatives open
to him, much can change in the course of four decades to
render these assumptions unrealistic, especially as progress
continues in the use of special feed additives.

There remains the problem of determining the extent to
which grazing land can satisfy the demand for roughage.
About one-half of the entire land surface of the continental
United States is used for grazing—more than twice as much
as for cropland. Some is used intensively, some marginally.

Of the roughly 1,000 million acres that support some kind of grazing about 7 per cent is farm pasture; about 70 per cent is in range and open permanent pasture. The balance is woodland and forest. Woodland grazing, whether on farms or not, yields so little in terms of nutrients that the effect is insignificant; accordingly, some students of land use prefer to think of no more than 700 million acres as grazing land.

How much feed can in the future come from grazing areas depends on the extent to which yields can be boosted. For the time being it would be rash to assume that rangeland yields will improve as much as hay or cropland pasture. We have put increases in the yield of open permanent farm pasture at less than 50 and of nonfarm rangeland at less than 30 per cent between 1960 and the end of the century, compared to 75 per cent for hay and cropland pasture. Whatever roughage demand remains unsatisfied at those yields would have to be met by cropland pasture.

Unharvested land.   Not all farmland is cropped or pastured every year. Some is left deliberately idle, while other land fails to produce a crop. This unharvested land forms as much a part of the farm as the acres that are cropped or grazed.

In the past twenty years, between 2 and 4 per cent of the cropland used for crops each year has not been harvested because of damage from insects or disease or because of adverse weather conditions. In periods of drought the proportion has risen to as much as 7 per cent, and in the mid-1930's it was over 10 per cent. While it can be expected that the insect and disease hazards will be considerably lessened in the years ahead, and that some of the weather hazards, the greatest threat, can be overcome, probably some 2 to 3 per cent of the land planted to crops each year must be counted on to produce nothing.

In the nation's semiarid region, some land is cultivated fallow each year in an effort to prevent the growth of weeds and rebuild soil moisture. The acreage left fallow in future years will in all probability never exceed 30 million acres, and it is quite possible that it will decline to as little as 15 million.

Finally, allowance must be made for cropland that each year is put under soil improvement or cover crops, or lies idle. The amount of land so treated has in the past been small, at least on the national level; in recent years it has averaged just below 20 million acres, the major portion of it idle.

How much cropland is needed? We are now ready to ask: how many acres are likely to be needed during the rest of the century to grow the crops to meet the nation's requirements for food, feed, and fiber? Many variables are included in this question—the kind of diet Americans will prefer in the future; how efficiently feed will be converted to meat, dairy, and other products; future crop yields; the division of feed between feed grains and pasturing.

Because of the many variables, the answer is varied, too. Will the demand be extremely low, or moderately low, or medium, or moderately high, or extremely high? Will the yields be high, low, or medium? What about feed efficiency? Starting from a figure of 470 million acres of available cropland—which has been the average over most of the fifties— an extremely low demand with high yields would give us a surplus of 216 million acres by 2000; an extremely high demand with low yields would give us a statistical "deficit" of more than half a billion acres by 2000! But these are unlikely combinations.

On the basis of the medium projection for demand, yield, and feed efficiency, 1980 will have an excess of cropland over combined crop and pasture needs of some 27 million acres— 4 million more than in 1960 (see Table 7). Thus, American farmers are likely to face the same kinds of problems over the next twenty years that they deal with today. By the year 2000, the picture changes. With demand registering 476 million acres, the excess acreage has disappeared. Instead, there is a deficit of 6 million acres. (And this changes but little when the three variables are either all high or low.) Had the projections been extended, they would undoubtedly have suggested significant deficits of cropland in the subsequent decades.

This statistical deficit tells us that, on the basis of the medium assumptions, more cropland will have to be "created" by more efficient production of food, feed, and fiber. The agriculture revolution must continue if Americans are to maintain and improve their current ways of living through the last years of the century. And improvement of the range may come into increasing prominence as a way of relieving any pressure upon cropland.

Table 7. How Cropland Needs for Crops and Pasture Might Vary under Different Assumptions for the Years 1980 and 2000

Demand for products	Low			Medium	High		
Unit yield	M	L	L	Medium	H	H	M
Feed efficiency	H	H	L	Medium	H	L	L
Cropland required							
1980 (mil. acres)	294	348	467	443	403	573	632
2000 (mil. acres)	283	336	475	476	462	762	857

Forest Land

Growing of trees constitutes the second largest category of land use. In the 48 contiguous states almost 490 million acres are in commercial forest land. Another 160 million acres consist of forest land not commercially exploited for timber production. Hence, about one-third of the land surface is in forest.

A look at the forest cover map in Figure 43 shows a large, practically treeless area with only small islands of forest lands preventing an almost complete separation of East and West. But that is not the main reason why the future of timber production is best discussed separately for Eastern and Western United States. For one thing, Western stands are old, including millions of acres of virgin forests, and the bulk of forest land is in public ownership. This compares with second and third growth in the East, and the predominance of private ownership and management. The importance of these factors is discussed below.

In addition, the geographical separation coincides largely with a distinction between hardwood, grown almost exclusively in the East, and softwood, grown predominantly in the West. The leading softwoods are Douglas fir, Southern yellow pine, and ponderosa pine. Oak is a principal commercial hardwood. Since hardwoods and softwoods are not easily interchangeable in most applications, they are best looked at separately in gauging the future adequacy. Another important distinction, especially to the lumber trade, is that between sawtimber and poletimber. Sawtimber is defined as trees of commercial species large enough and otherwise suitable to be sawn into lumber; minimum specifications range from 9 to 11 inches at breast height, depending on type and region. Poletimber is growing stock of less than sawtimber size but at least 5 inches in diameter at breast height.

The nation's inventory of growing stock is supplemented by a sizable amount of nongrowing stock, such as cull trees, salvageable dead trees, and usable tops and limbs. In a growing forest, this inventory is continuously replenished by young growth that reaches the required minimum size of 5-inch diameter. It then graduates into poletimber and is counted as part of the growing stock—by far the largest source of supply.

Tree growth vs. cut. Because trees require a very long time to mature and become commercially useful there is no immediately obvious counterpart to the annual requirement estimate, such as in cotton, wheat, or other products of the soil. Few species take as little as twenty or twenty-five years; many take forty or fifty years before they can be profitably cut. In order to compare requirements with supply, one esti-

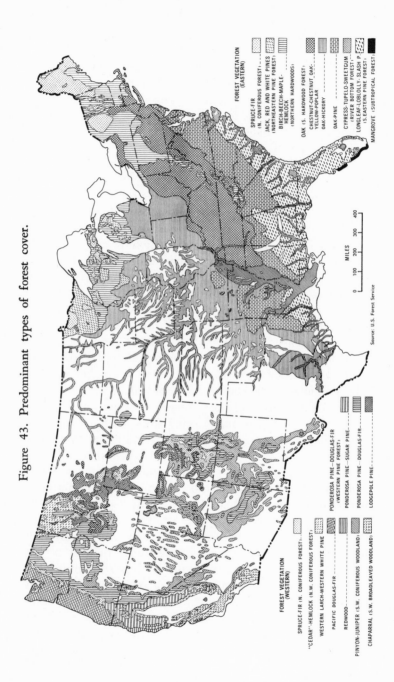

Figure 43. Predominant types of forest cover.

FOREST VEGETATION (WESTERN)

SPRUCE-FIR (N. CONIFEROUS FOREST)
"CEDAR"-HEMLOCK (N.W. CONIFEROUS FOREST)
WESTERN LARCH-WESTERN WHITE PINE
PACIFIC DOUGLAS-FIR
REDWOOD
PINYON-JUNIPER (S.W. CONIFEROUS WOODLAND)
CHAPARRAL (S.W. BROADLEAVED WOODLAND)

PONDEROSA PINE-DOUGLAS-FIR (WESTERN PINE FOREST)
PONDEROSA PINE-SUGAR PINE
PONDEROSA PINE-DOUGLAS-FIR
LODGEPOLE PINE

FOREST VEGETATION (EASTERN)

SPRUCE-FIR (N. CONIFEROUS FOREST)
JACK, RED AND WHITE PINES (NORTHEASTERN PINE FOREST)
BIRCH-BEECH-MAPLE-HEMLOCK (NORTHERN HARDWOODS)
OAK (S. HARDWOOD FOREST)
CHESTNUT-CHESTNUT OAK-YELLOW-POPLAR
OAK-HICKORY
OAK-PINE
CYPRESS-TUPELO-SWEETGUM (RIVER BOTTOM FOREST)
LONGLEAF-LOBLOLLY-SLASH P. (S. EASTERN PINE FOREST)
MANGROVE (SUBTROPICAL FOREST)

Source: U.S. Forest Service

0   100   200   300   400
MILES

mates the quantity of the tree "crop," that is, the year's growth, less the amount of timber in trees lost by disease, fire, and other natural causes.

But the rate of growth, as well as the absolute volume of growth, are affected by the size of the annual cut. Consequently, one must calculate, as a continuous chain, the effect of a year's net growth and cut on the total inventory. The inventory at the end of the period, in turn, becomes the starting inventory of the next, and so on.

Small variations in the growth rate, because of the very large inventory of growing trees, will make substantial differences in the inventory. To illustrate, in 1952, when the last nationwide survey was made, the nation's Western forests had a growing stock of 273 billion cubic feet. The rate of growth at that time was just about 1 per cent, or 2.74 billion cubic feet. The year's cut, on the other hand, amounted to 3.75 billion cubic feet, or 1 billion more than the net growth. Had the Western growth been 1.5 per cent instead of the recorded 1 per cent, then the volume of growth would have been more nearly 4.1 billion, with the result that the inventory of trees in the West, instead of dropping, would have been increasing.

East and West: fast vs. slow growth. Regional factors are of great importance in forest policy and management. The starting inventory, the rate of growth, and the cut that is made each year are intimately related, and where these elements vary between different regions, accounting in aggregate terms becomes less meaningful. Broadly speaking, well-planned cutting in the West promotes rather than inhibits future growth, since much of the inventory is of advanced age and contributes little or nothing to growth. Western states contain a larger proportion of sawtimber than the East, and a stand of sawtimber will have a lower growth than a stand of younger and smaller trees. In addition, most of the Western commercial forest area supports original growth, of which the giant redwoods and sequoias of California are the most publicized. Over a large area, such stands tend to achieve a balance of little if any net growth. Whatever growth there is, mostly from the roots of old growth, is balanced by decay and death. The West, including coastal Alaska, is estimated to have close to 50 million acres of old-growth sawtimber; over 40 per cent of this is unexploited virgin forest. Thus, an abundance of inventory holds down the volume of growth in the West, and consequently the rate of growth is low.

In the East the situation is quite different. The inventory is relatively small and the rate of growth high. Because there is so little old growth left in the East, the rate of growth in relation to inventory is much higher than it is in the West. On the other hand, the total volume of trees and above all the quality of growth in the East could be much higher were it not for the understocking; for the East contains most of the nation's inadequately utilized, poorly stocked or nonstocked, commercial forest land. To summarize the differences, the total annual volume of growth is held down in the West by an abundance of old stands that grow but little, and in the East by the small size of the forest resource. Nonetheless, because the growth rate in the East is about six times that in the West, the volume of the annual increment is much larger in the East than in the West.

As for the third element in the equation, the annual cut, it is divided pretty evenly between the West and the East, despite the fact that the bulk of demand is for softwood and the bulk of the softwood stands are in the West. However, these are not only relatively remote from any but the Western markets, but being largely publicly owned and managed are less responsive to market forces.

In calculating the combined effect of the annual balance of growth and cut upon forest stands and upon future annual growth, it follows from the explanations given above that, if the annual cut exceeds the annual growth, the rate of growth will rise in the West, but will decrease in the East.

This broad generalization is important in understanding the consequences for the forest inventory that we examine below.

How can projected demand for timber products be met in the next forty years? Obviously, in two ways: by harvesting the net growth only, or by eating into capital through harvesting beyond that level.

The forest inventory. By the year 2000 demand for domestic forest products is projected at over 29 billion cubic feet and net growth at only a little over 12 billion. Can new forests be planted in sufficient quantity to plug this gap of 17 billion cubic feet? The U.S. Forest Service estimates that some 55 cubic feet of realizable growth can be harvested from one acre of commercial forest land. On that basis, some 300 million acres would have to be planted to fill the gap, and they would have to be planted soon. New technology, such as faster breeding, higher rates of fertilization, etc., might reduce this figure, but not substantially. Furthermore, much of the land converted to forest would be in small lots, scattered over the country, with little relationship to points of processing or consumption. Further shrinkage of commercial forest land is generally believed to be ahead. Hence, the projected demand is incompatible with preservation of the nation's forests. Table 8 shows projected demand for timber products and the effect on domestic forests, with separate figures for the East and the West, and for softwood and hardwood.

Looking first at softwoods, let us assume that, for the rest of the century, half the supplies will continue to come from the West and half from the East. Under this assumption, Eastern forests will remain substantially stable through 1980, but will undergo rapid depletion thereafter (see Figure 44). Western forests will hold up better for a while, but by the end of the century they too will be rapidly moving towards depletion. This would not be serious through the 1980's if it could be assumed that the Western cut will be substantially from old stands that contribute little to growth anyway. The

Table 8. Effect upon Growing Stock of Meeting the Demand for Forest Products

(bil. cu. ft. roundwood)

Item	Softwood			Hardwood		
	1960	1980	2000	1960	1980	2000
Demand, net of imports	7.5	12.3	21.7	3.1	4.3	7.4
Cut from East	3.7	6.1	10.8⎞			
Cut from West	3.7	6.1	10.8⎠	3.1	4.3	7.4
Net growth in East	4.6	4.1	nil⎞			
Net growth in West	2.5	3.6	2.4⎠	8.0	10.0	10.0
Growing stock in East	79	72	nil⎞			
Growing stock in West	253	219	121⎠	192	299	389

shortage thereafter, however, would have to be met by cutting trees that are still adding volume, thus depleting the capital stock.

Many other assumptions concerning the cut and growth rate can be made. A shift from softwood to hardwood is an important one, since hardwood supplies are relatively abundant and a change in the balance would take the pressure off the softwood areas. But all assumptions except the most optimistic (which is labeled (3) in Figure 44) would see Eastern forests on the way to extinction by 2000. In the West, there would be gradual depletion. But by the end of the century, even in the West, the volume of the cut would be so large as to make it difficult to avoid cutting into the younger growing stands—and hence depleting capital.

In purely statistical terms the hardwood situation presents at first a more favorable picture. Net growth can more than furnish the volume demanded. As a consequence the volume of growing stock would continue to increase, and the rate of growth would decline somewhat, but not enough to bring about a reversal of this trend by the end of the century. The real problem is not, however, one of quantity but of

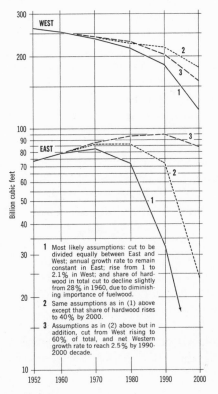

Figure 44. How different patterns of cutting and growth would affect growing stock of softwood.

quality. The Eastern hardwood stands—the country's principal source—are in various stages of regrowth, following logging and fires. There is a dearth of sawtimber, the most desirable product, and much of the stock is of poor quality and fit for only limited markets.

The situation is even less promising when one looks at demands for specific types, qualities, and species of wood. The outlook for over-all adequacy during the next two decades or so thus carries no implication that specific shortages would not arise. Of these, the pressure on sawtimber—not shown in our calculations—is probably the most significant. However, it may be less severe than suggested by the "supply gap" evident in the figures relating to total timber products. Pulpwood, which does not require sawtimber-size trees, constitutes a growing portion of demand. Also, there is the impressive volume of timber residues, which could, with improved, lower-cost methods of collecting and delivery, be brought to pulp mills—the amount of residue available adds up to 40 per cent of estimated pulp demand in 1960. Only two-thirds of plant residues—suitable for a long list of end products, from brush handles to fiberboard—is used at all, and of this nearly nine-tenths is burned as fuel. Finally, shifts to hardwood pulp and to hardwood generally might prove feasible beyond the limits set in our projects. But none of these potential sources of supply appears large enough to hold out the prospect that demand for forest products as a whole could be met through the end of the century without depleting the softwood inventory.

Imports. Imports of pulpwood and its products have been significant in the U.S. market for years; lumber imports have become so more recently. Not counting imports of newsprint, which have been running between 5 and 6 million tons a year for the last decade, and are projected to rise to over 7 million tons by the end of the century, imports of timber and timber products have accounted for 10 to 15 per cent of consumption, the great bulk of it softwood. Since domestic forests could supply the projected demand only under very unlikely assumptions (see Figure 44), imports represent a possible avenue of escape. The most obvious source, as in the past, would be Canada, especially for pulpwood and pulpwood products. Western Europe will most likely be in a deficit position, and will attempt equally to draw on Canadian supplies. The Soviet Union has a vast supply of softwood—larger than that of any other country in the world—but accessibility greatly limits the export potential. In addition, Western Europe rather than the United States would probably be first in line as a customer.

In making the projections we have probably stretched potential imports of Canadian softwood to the limit by assuming that by the end of the century U.S. imports might have risen to 3 billion cubic feet of roundwood. This is almost four times the 1960 amount, and there is serious question whether such quantities will in fact become available.

As on the domestic scene, so on a global scale, a shift from softwood to hardwood opens up a more favorable perspective. In Canada, the allowable cut of hardwood for 1980 has been estimated at over 2 billion cubic feet in excess of domestic demands. Since in our projections we have assumed net hardwood imports by 1980 at less than 10 per cent that amount, one might view this Canadian excess as a possible way of closing or at least narrowing the supply gap, provided hardwood can be made increasingly acceptable. Another source of hardwood, so far little explored and less exploited, is the tropical and semitropical forests of South America and Africa. As increasing attention is paid by developing countries to their forest resources, one may expect them to develop not only their domestic market, but also their export potential. To the extent that hardwood becomes acceptable, new sources of imports for the United States, and for other deficit areas, may emerge. Failing such adaptation it is extremely difficult to see any adjustment other than substitution of nonforest material.

The impact of tightening supplies. If, as appears likely, a substantial part of the projected U.S. demand for timber cannot be met in the latter part of this century, and wood will be available only at rising prices, what is to be done about it? Some possible solutions have already been mentioned: increased rates of timber growth, shifts in geographic source, general improvements in management, and increased imports. Also in view are intensified exploration of tropical forests, investigation of the qualities of tropical trees, further promotion of economies in the use of wood, the utilization of waste, and the substitution of other materials.

Possibilities of substitution of other materials for forest products are large and widening. Important developments may include the increasing use of such construction materials as brick and concrete, aluminum, plastics, and fiberglass; use of nonwood vegetable fibers such as sugarcane bagasse in making paper; use of aluminum foil and plastics instead of paper for packing, and of nonwood materials for boxing and crating; perhaps a basic change in shipping methods, eliminating the use of boxing.

All the above may seem strange in the face of a timber market that has in recent years experienced stable and even falling prices. Timber producers, far from scanning the horizon for sources of supply, view imports as threatening the domestic market and are generally pessimistic about the future market for their own trees. As a matter of fact, however, their practical business sense and the projections summarized above are not necessarily in conflict. Up to 1980, no notable decline in inventory is apparent, and demand builds up so gradually that it can easily be met—at least in the aggregate. Certain species may be subject to rising costs and prices even before 1980, and there may be some substitution between species and between sawtimber and poletimber.

The projections to 1980, consequently, are compatible with the practical lumberman's concern about marketing his product. It is only as one looks beyond the halfway mark that imbalance begins to appear. But this is one of the advantages of trying to look so far ahead. As a result of looking now, by the time 1980 rolls around enough shifts may have occurred in both the economy and the technology of lumbering to make us readjust our ideas about the declining forest inventory.

Urban Land

In 1960 nearly seven out of ten Americans were urban residents, but their direct impact upon land use was surprisingly small. Only a little more than 1 per cent of all land in the United States could be classified as urban, and of this land between one-third and one-half is not in actual use, though unlikely ever again to revert to farming, grazing, or forestry. Urban land—defined as land withdrawn from alternative uses—amounted to not quite 17 million acres in 1950, and had risen by 1960 to over 21 million acres. Doubling, or a little better, is the outlook for the year 2000.

Urban density as well as urban land has increased, but very gradually. From 1850 to 1950, urban population density increased around 20 per cent, while urban population grew about 2,500 per cent. Urban density is estimated as increasing further, but at a declining rate of speed.

The broad significance of urban areas lies in their effect on the economy and on the environment they create—not on their demand for land, which is minor, viewed in the context of total demand. They pose problems of social organization, of transportation, and so forth, but they will hardly be a factor in the sufficiency of land within the next forty years.

Transportation

Transportation demand covers land set aside for railroads, airports, highways, and so on. Railroad rights-of-way now occupy about 8 million acres, and no increase is foreseen. The amount of land occupied by highways and adjacent rights-of-way, on the other hand, will undoubtedly grow from the present 16 million acres. The federal superhighway program alone might require as much as 2 million additional acres. By the end of the century, including provision for additional airports and landing strips, land set aside for transportation services might increase by 4 million acres over the 1960 level.

The Great Outdoors

The fast-growing demand for outdoor recreation is likely to create heavy pressure for land. Rising population and income, more rapid transportation, and increased leisure time have combined to send a rapidly growing stream of urban residents to the great outdoors.

The increase in the number of annual visits to outdoor recreation facilities has rarely fallen below 10 per cent in recent years. If one were to project this trend into the future, one would arrive at a demand for outdoor recreation that would take up much of the time of most of the population, as well as a great share of the land. By the year 2000 the present trend would imply, for instance, over three visits each year by every man, woman, and child in the United States to a national park, and some 9 billion visits, or better than two visits per person each month, to the national forests and state parks. At the other end of the scale, if the number of visits grows only in proportion to the projected increases in population and income, one arrives at a kind of floor. The medium estimates used here are midway between these two extremes. This medium rate works out to an annual growth of somewhere between 6 and 8 per cent, according to types of area. The fastest increase would be in visits to national forests, the slowest would be in visits to national parks (see Table 9).

To keep the projection within reason, a more intensive use of existing facilities has been assumed—better than doubling in intensity between 1960 and 1980, and again between 1980 and 2000—except for state parks, where it is assumed visits per acre will rise only about half as fast because of the already high intensity of use. This more intense use reduces the demand for acreage but means more investment in access roads, camping and picnicking facilities, roads and trails, development of water supplies, sewage facilities, and so on.

Table 9. Visits to Principal Recreation Areas

(Per thousand population)

Year		National parks, monuments, and recreation areas	National forests	State parks
1920		9	n.a.	n.a.
1940		82	122	n.a.
1946[1]		97	129	534
1950		144	180	753
1960		229	516	1,439
1980[2]	Low	330	750	2,100
	Medium	520	1,760	3,460
	High	820	3,840	5,820
2000[2]	Low	490	1,110	3,100
	Medium	1,180	6,070	8,370
	High	2,340	19,820	18,290

n.a. Not available.

1. First full postwar year.

2. Growth rates calculated as follows: Low—at rate of growth in per capita disposable income; High—basically extension of 1946-60 trend, slightly reduced after 1980; Medium—halfway between two extremes.

Much will depend on public policy and on the willingness of users to substitute second and third choices for their first choice. Such a substitution would be difficult in areas like Yosemite National Park or Grand Canyon National Park. In most national parks and forests and many of the state parks, however, it should be possible to add greatly to the intensity of use and therefore to total carrying capacity.

Increases in intensity would involve sacrifices and compromises. Large populations of wildlife are incompatible with large numbers of people. A more elaborate grading of park and forest areas—ranging from wilderness to highly developed camping and picnicking areas, would be helpful.

Even allowing for growth in intensity of use, the projected number of visits will still require substantially increased acreage. At the moment, excluding reservoir areas and city parks, the acreage suitable principally for recreation in national and state parks and national forests amounts to about 45 million acres. For the national parks system, the national forests, and the state parks jointly, we would have to add 32 million acres by 1980, and 57 million more by 2000—totaling about 90 million acres to be added between now and the end of the century.

Many people doubt whether such large physical increases are feasible. The cost per acre is rising, and demand for other types of use will grow as the population increases and the economy develops. More likely than such large physical expansion will be the multiple use of land now used mainly for other purposes—such as growing trees.

Short of an increase in intensity of use or in acreage, or a combination of the two, growth in demand would have to be checked or redistributed through various schemes of rationing. Limitations on length of stay, higher fees for entrance and use, vigorous efforts to spread the use over less popular portions of the week, month, and year—all might have to come into play. To some extent, the pressure on public recreation lands could, of course, be eased by increases in private facilities. But information both on the physical and economic aspects of privately owned land, lakes, and beaches is still far too meager to warrant speculation on this score, despite pioneering efforts made by the Outdoor Recreation Resources Review Commission.

Pressures on the Land

The projected increases in land requirements for uses other than agriculture and forestry and recreation are some 40 million acres between 1960 and 2000. This includes 10-15 million acres for wildlife refuges and water reservoirs.

For 1980, there is sufficient acreage in sight to satisfy these mounting needs: a surplus of cropland of perhaps as much as 25 million acres, plus some 10-15 million acres that might be squeezed out of residual land—wetlands, mountains, deserts, etc.

Most of the rising demand will be for the land located near urban centers. Thus good cropland may be lost to suburban sprawl, and the attainment of high national yields may be that much more difficult. Less serious would be loss of grazing land to nonagricultural uses, which could be replaced by a far smaller acreage of cropland elsewhere, or the loss of low fertility cropland in areas of reservoir and wildlife expansion. Fortunately, whatever the paths of adjustment, the prospective surplus of cropland through 1980 is large enough to permit expansion of other uses, even with a moderate amount of frictional loss in the process of substitution.

When demand for recreation acreage is included, this picture changes. The more than 30 million acres demanded by recreation through 1980 can be drawn only from residual land, or from land now serving some other purpose.

By the year 2000, satisfaction of all projected demands would mean the use of every acre in the 48 contiguous states, including deserts, mountain peaks, and marshes. Even at that, there would result a net shortage of 50 million acres. But since one must assume that there exists a rock-bottom acreage of true wasteland, not good for anything—and this can hardly be less than 60 million acres—the unsatisfied demand for land totals more nearly 110 million acres.

Among the items that generate this demand are a rise between 1980 and 2000 of over 30 million acres in cropland needs, and continuing expansion of nonagricultural demand, especially recreation. But even without growth in recreation land areas after 1980, demand for all uses would exceed the usable acreage by the sizable amount of some 50 million acres.

The renewed increase of cropland demand between 1980 and 2000 would call for inroads on permanent pasture, and thus pose problems of capital investment for land improvement as well as possible regional shifts.

The shortfall in acreage emerging by the end of the century suggests the need, on the one hand, for multiple use of land, and on the other, for intensification of range management.

The demand for additional recreation acreage finds expression largely through public action channels, and is likely to call for increased investment in facilities far more than in land. Hence, recreation demands may become a balancing factor. Pressure from urban growth is moderate, and will be satisfied through the interplay of market forces and public policy. Pressure from cropland does not become a factor until the second half of the forty-year period. On the other hand, if any of the 300 million acres estimated as needed to satisfy the projected demand for forest products were to be included, the balancing of land demand and supply would become unmanageable long before 2000.

On the black-ink side of the ledger are no less than 215 million acres of land in the top three soil classes most fitted for crop raising, which are now in either grassland or woodland. From the purely physical point of view, therefore, there appears ample room for extending the present crop acreage, should the need arise. Deliberate shifts in acreage, based on soil capability, are another means of "creating" acres. The conversion to cropland of grazing land and noncommercial forest land, especially in the South, which now renders at best a low yield of animal feed, would help satisfy expanding acreage demand. Such shifts will in all likelihood entail investment in irrigation and soil-building practices. Thus we have a choice of paths, and a number of possible "ways out" towards the goal of adequacy of land resources for all the demands likely to be made in the next forty years.

Table 10 brings together in one place all the information developed above on current and future requirements for land.

Table 10. Land Use, 1950 and 1960, and Projections for 1980 and 2000

(Million acres)

Land use	1950	1960	1980	2000
Cropland, including pasture[1]	478	447	443	476
Grazing land[1]	700	700	700	700
Farmland, non-producing	45	45	45	45
Commercial forest land[2]	484	484	484	484
Recreation (excluding reservoir areas and city parks)	42	44	76	134
Urban (including city parks)	17	21	32	45
Transportation	25	26	28	30
Wildlife refuge	14	15	18	20
Reservoirs	10	12	15	20
Total specified[2]	1,815	1,794	1,841	1,954
Other land (residual)	89	110	63	−50
Total land area	1,904	1,904	1,904	1,904

1. All adjustments for feeding requirements are made in cropland, with grazing land held constant.

2. Does not provide for increased acreage to meet projected commercial forest demand. Requirements to close the projected gap in 2000 might run as high as 300 million acres to be put into forest use at this time.

The growing pressure of total demand upon land resources stands out clearly, as well as the diminishing factor of "other land," which will shrink considerably by 1980 and by the end of the century acquire a minus sign. This points once again to multiple use of substantial tracts of land as a means of meeting projected requirements.

ENERGY

In 1960 the United States consumed about 45 quadrillion Btu of energy. If this had all been supplied from one source it would have required 1¾ billion tons of coal (over four times the tonnage actually produced), or 8 billion barrels of oil (over three times the amount produced). By the end of the century, this country is likely to be consuming about three times as much each year, and the cumulative total demand for energy during the 40-year period between 1960 and 2000 is estimated at 3,300 quadrillion Btu—the equivalent of either 130 billion tons of coal, close to 600 billion barrels of oil, or 3,200 trillion cubic feet of natural gas.

The only fuel that could single-handedly supply this huge amount of energy is coal. No one has so far suggested recoverable oil or gas supplies in the United States amounting to more than half the cumulative totals shown. But according to recent estimates of the U.S. Department of the Interior current recovery methods would allow over 200 billion tons of bituminous coal to be mined at current prices. Others have put the figure even higher. Total coal resources of the United States—that is, the amount that might reasonably become recoverable with improved technology—amount to some 1,700 billion tons.

While the thought of that much coal in the ground is a comforting one, the art of gasifying and liquefying it would have to be advanced far beyond the present stage to enable it to fill economically the 40 per cent of total energy demand now met by oil and the 30 per cent met by gas. What is more relevant, therefore, in an appraisal of the adequacy of energy, is a look at the resources of all fuels, and other sources of energy while keeping in mind that there is in the background this vast storehouse of bituminous coal. Since oil is presently the largest single source of energy in the United States, and also has been the object of most controversy, we shall begin this inquiry with oil. We shall then take a look at some possible substitutes—coal, shale oil, and tar sands— before coming to natural gas, another fuel the adequacy of which is by no means certain. Nonfuel sources—hydro and nuclear, and new sources and techniques—close this section.

Crude Oil

A typical U.S. oil field consists of hard rock formation or sometimes highly compacted sand with oil lodged in tiny pores. Oil-soaked rock is perhaps a better picture of an oil field than is conveyed by the industry's term "pool." Exploitation of an oil field, once it is discovered through geology, geophysics, geochemistry, etc., is more than simply punching a hole in the reservoir and letting the contents gush out. Less than one-third of the oil in place, it is estimated, has actually been recovered from developed fields. The remainder must be driven out by various methods—mainly water, fire, and different gases—developed in the last two decades. And, even then, substantial amounts are never dislodged.

Proved reserves. There have been unceasing attempts to estimate the size of the country's total oil resources. Petroleum history is littered with the remains of obsolete guesses some of which have turned out to be spectacularly wrong. One of the reasons is that only that relatively small part of oil occurrences that exploratory drilling has proved to exist can be correctly said to be "known." Beyond, short of systematically digging up the first 60,000 feet of the earth's crust from pole to pole, one can go only by inference.

Another reason is that too much attention has been focused on "proved reserves," now totaling about 32 billion barrels. These are but the current working stock or inventory of unrecovered petroleum carried by the producers for the accomplishment of rational commercial operations. They take into account, broadly speaking, only those reserves in known fields believed to be producible at current prices and at current levels of technology. Hence, proved reserves have increased in proportion to production; demand has continuously "created" the supply to meet it. But as a measure of a country's oil resources, proved reserves are inadequate and misleading.

Ultimate reserves. A more useful concept is that of the so-called "ultimate reserves," which include the sum of past production, current proved reserves, and reserves that will be discovered in the future. The weakness of this measure is that—like proved reserves—it does not allow for improved technology, and therefore has a conservative bias. If, however, one could arrive at a consensus from the many estimates of the ultimate reserves, then subtract the petroleum produced in the past, the amount of oil potentially available in the future could be derived. In arithmetical terms, it would be the ultimate reserves minus past production, divided by the recovery factor.

The resource base. The outcome of these calculations has been called the "resource base." It is a measure of the occurrence of the material in nature, diminished by past production. This represents barrels of oil in the ground awaiting future recovery. Its magnitude may be in the neighborhood of 500 billion barrels. If future recovery rates are no better than in the past—an unrealistic assumption—not more than 160 or 170 billion barrels would be recovered of this amount. But recovery rates have grown substantially, and there is no reason to believe that they will not increase further. If one assumes, for instance, that the average rate of recoverability will rise to two-thirds over time, the resulting amount of oil in the ground that can eventually be lifted will be 330 billion barrels. If the recovery rate rises to only one-half, the amount lifted will be only 250 billion barrels.

These estimates are not predictions, nor do they even imply the likelihood that such amounts will in fact be recovered. Recovery will depend on a variety of factors, including relative price movements, government policy, and technological factors in production, distribution, and consumption. Recoverability estimates are useful mainly as a benchmark that can be compared with cumulative demand. But demand itself is another kind of benchmark, possible of attainment only under certain conditions. Before cumulative demand can be compared with possible supply, another factor must be added —a provision for supporting reserves. It is inconceivable that oil companies would produce oil at such a high rate without being sure of having large reserves in the ground.

Can demand be met? Cumulative demand alone over the next forty years will probably remain substantially below even the minimum recoverable supplies of 250 billion barrels, and amount to not much more than half the maximum recoverable supplies of 330 billion barrels.

But the moment that provision is made for reserves to support production, the picture changes radically. Cumulative demand plus supporting reserves would by the year 2000 exceed minimum recoverable supplies, and would come dangerously close to the maximum. As a consequence, it would be necessary in the decade beginning in 1980 to prove nearly half the then remaining reserves of petroleum in this country, assuming that the lower total—250 billion barrels—reflects the limits of recoverability. Even at the recoverability level of 330 billion barrels, 30 per cent of all remaining reserves would have to be found and proved in the 1980's. Figure 45 shows these implications of projected demand for domestic oil, assuming a continuing 20 per cent import quota.

Regardless of cost considerations, reserve additions would be likely to slow down and reverse direction long before the year 2000. So would production. Beyond 1980, things would become difficult.

This estimate jibes with a recent one by Paul Torrey of the Interstate Oil Compact Commission, a geologist whose judgment is widely respected in the industry. He ventures the estimate that of the original oil content of known U.S. reservoirs—which in 1960 he put at 328 billion barrels— almost 30 per cent, or 90 billion barrels, are either in proved reserves or are recoverable by secondary methods. When compared with the demand estimates made here, production

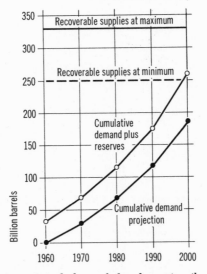

Figure 45. How projected demand for domestic oil compares with estimated recoverable supplies in the United States.

of this supply would take us safely through the next two decades. Moreover, when past production, equal to 20 per cent of the original content, is added, the resulting recovery factor is 50 per cent.

Adequacy of resources and expected advances in techniques of exploration and recovery suggest no reason why, from a resource point of view, the price of domestic crude should not stay in line with the general price level for the next fifteen or twenty years. After 1975 or 1980, however, stringent domestic resource conditions might more than offset technological advances, with consequent pressures on price. Much will depend on the ingenuity of the industry in finding and recovering domestic oil resources, the sufficiency of the financial rewards, and the outlook for competing sources.

Domestic oil has vigorous competition—both from other fuels and from foreign production. Should costs of oil-finding increase and not be offset by cost-saving in other phases of the industry, and the price of domestic oil be thus pushed ahead of competing energy sources, such a development would force growing competition from lower-priced imported crude; from coal, either directly or by way of electricity; from new conversion methods in transportation, such as efficient batteries; and from domestic and Canadian shale or tar sands.

Oil imports. Even now close to 20 per cent of U.S. petroleum demand is met by imports. The main reason they are not increasing is that government control has been freezing them at a level between 15 and 20 per cent for the last several years. The lower cost at which they can be sold in the United States suggests that without such controls foreign oil would by now have captured a much higher share of the market.

If it is difficult to project domestic supply and demand, the difficulties are multiplied many times when the focus is enlarged to encompass the entire world, or even just the non-Communist world. Shifts in energy demand in the developed countries, especially Western Europe, have been of striking magnitude since the end of World War II. By and large, they have paralleled the earlier experience of the United States. Oil and to a much lesser extent natural gas have continuously encroached on the markets previously held by coal. European observers believe that this will continue, at least for some time. Meanwhile, the progress of nuclear energy, which at first seemed to be much faster than in the United States, is beset by the same uncertainty abroad as here. Moreover, European oil consumption depends largely on imports, and adequacy must be considered in the context of worldwide future oil demand and supply. Finally, natural gas supplies have barely been tapped and are only beginning to have an impact on the energy pattern. Judging from recent discoveries, that impact may be substantial.

The greatest unknown variable, however, is the future consumption in the developing countries of Asia and Africa, and to some extent Latin America. Here one is apt to be carried away by the figures conjured up from prospective population growth and industrial expansion. While the potential oil needs of the developing countries are of course enormous, their demand is unlikely to gather enough momentum in the next forty years to affect crucially the world demand picture. Even in the Soviet Union, after forty years of intensive industrial development, annual consumption of oil is less than 4 barrels per capita—about one-fifth what it is in the United States. The average Japanese consumes only 2½ barrels per year, compared with 20 barrels per capita in the United States, despite the fact that in recent years Japanese consumption has grown at more than 20 per cent per year.

At least as impressive as the large increase in oil consumption outside the United States is the vast expansion in reserves and resources of foreign oil. Middle East oil reserves have increased 4½ times since 1950, and recent exploration of offshore locations in the Persian Gulf has further cemented the area's predominance. The Middle East had in 1960 proved reserves of an estimated 185 billion barrels—equivalent to about 60 times the total amount of the petroleum products consumed in the United States in 1960, or about 125 times consumption in Western Europe. Reserves of the world as a whole stand at about 300 billion barrels.

Vast changes have occurred in the distribution of oil reserves in the last twenty-five years. The Middle East now accounts for over 60 per cent, the United States for only 10 per cent. Before World War II, the United States accounted for 40 per cent, the Middle East for 30. While the appearance of North Africa as a supply area has injected a new element, it will take a long time for this or any other new development to affect the predominance of the Middle East. Figure 46 shows some of these shifts.

Political factors also will determine future supply. Much of the world's oil is located in politically unstable areas, sub-

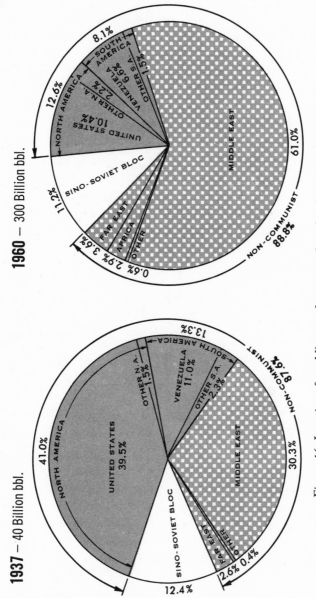

1937 — 40 Billion bbl.

1960 — 300 Billion bbl.

Figure 46. Location of world's proved reserves of crude oil, 1937 and 1960.

ject to domestic upheavals and uncertain in their continuance
as parts of the non-Communist or uncommitted parts of the
globe. Most of the Middle East, the North African fields,
and Indonesia are in this condition. The question of continuing availability of supply at stable cost, which has long
plagued this country, is now of concern to Western Europe,
which draws nearly 80 per cent of its supplies from the Middle East.

Despite these problems, the United States could nonetheless obtain for some time to come a very much larger proportion of the oil it requires from abroad—perhaps as much as
a third, a half, or even more of its total requirements. Not
only the Middle East, but Venezuela, and in a few years
perhaps Canada, could supply much larger amounts of oil
to the United States than we import at present.

Coal

Coal is always ready to appear on any market in which its
price makes it attractive. It is difficult to see coal replacing
oil anywhere, however, except as an industrial fuel, which
includes, of course, electric power generation. Since industrial consumption is not an important segment of total oil
consumption except in petroleum refining, the effects of substitution of coal for oil in industry would not be very great.
In either transportation or home use, wholly new installations
and even techniques would be required to bring coal back
to its previous dominant position.

The United States has more than enough coal to meet any
increased demand that might result over the next forty years
if a shift in price relationships should cause some consumers
to shift from oil and gas to coal. To a large extent, the delivered
price of coal will depend on transportation technology and
policy, as they affect the rates established by its principal
carriers and sanctioned by governmental regulatory bodies,
such as the Interstate Commerce Commission. The anticipated concentration of coal demand in fewer uses—basically

electricity generation and the metallurgical industries—would seem to favor the emergence of consumer-oriented types of transportation that would not only prevent cost increases but bring about significant cost reduction. Recent instances of substantial reductions in railroad rates for coal suggest that this is happening. The extent to which new techniques may be applicable remains to be tested.

Costs might also be cut by linking coal mines to utilities, and possibly to other large consumers, by pipelines carrying a slurry of coal and water. This method was successfully used for several years in the 108-mile line that brought coal to the Cleveland Electric Illuminating Company. The line was recently closed down, when railroad rates were drastically reduced. More ambitious projects, such as moving heavy volumes of Appalachian coal to the Atlantic seaboard, are on the horizon but may be some time in coming into operation. The successful feeding of slurry directly to boilers would further lower the cost. Especially designed trains and new loading and unloading methods now being tried out would play an important part in lowering the price of coal to consumers, or at least in keeping it from rising. Long-distance extra-high-voltage powerlines are another way in which coal might increase its competitive advances. Modern technology has made it increasingly possible to transmit large blocks of power over long distances at costs that enable "coal-by-wire" to challenge other energy sources that are either closer or have lower transportation cost.

Altogether, it is difficult to see why delivered coal should undergo any price changes other than those that reflect cost changes at the mine. There, the continuing advances in cost-cutting mechanization, the past record of increases in output per man-day, and the likelihood that coal wages in the future will not increase with greater speed than wages generally, all suggest relative stability of costs for coal. Thus coal alone among the fuels could meet an even higher demand than the one projected here at current, and perhaps lower, prices.

Shale Oil and Tar Sands

Shale oil has a potential resource base that dwarfs that of crude oil: 1,000 billion recoverable barrels of oil, just from rock yielding at least 15 gallons per ton. If Canadian tar sands are added to the shale oil resources, any problem of adequacy of liquid fuel is shifted far into the next century, provided the techniques for recovering both types of fuel yield a competitive product.

Current experience here and abroad suggests that there are no technical obstacles to producing shale oil, even possibly shale gas, in commercial quantities. Pilot operations indicate the probability that oil could be produced and transported to West Coast locations at prices competitive with those of California crude. However, cost analysis has been based on relatively small pilot plants, and has not established beyond doubt the potential competitiveness of shale oil. There is also the question of sufficient water supply in those parts of the country which are candidates for production—predominantly the Colorado plateau—although success has been claimed for a dry process. Finally, a Colorado-based shale oil industry would have to overcome substantial odds to compete in locations other than the West Coast, due to the absence of low-cost water transportation of the kind enjoyed by Gulf producers in supplying the East Coast. However, a significant increase in the real price of crude, combined with the likelihood of a further advance, could stimulate the construction of large diameter pipelines and the acceptance of shale oil, provided sufficient capital could be channeled into shale oil exploitation and distribution.

The purchase or lease of sizable shale acreages in Colorado by a number of major oil companies bespeaks their long-run interest in the potential. For the moment, this is more in the nature of an insurance policy. Given the large and growing financial stake that most major producers have in foreign oil development, they would probably prefer to turn to imports rather than to shale and would apply their efforts toward abolishing import controls rather than toward building up a domestic shale industry. The fact that shale oil has been below the horizon for so long does not mean that it may not appear above it. But it is too soon to determine the timetable.

Bituminous—or tar—sands in Canada, located in the province of Alberta, are equally abundant sources of petroleum. Several large oil companies have declared themselves ready to commence mining and refining operations, but governmental permission has been slow in emerging largely due to the fact that outlets for Canadian crude oil are hard enough to come by so that enlarging the supply base is not an urgent business. A first, modest, operation is now expected to get under way in the near future.

Natural Gas

Estimates of recoverable supplies of natural gas are generally arrived at by estimating the volume of gas in ratio to the volume of oil as they occur in the ground, and then multiplying this ratio by the amount of oil judged to be potentially recoverable. (As in the case of oil, we notice only in passing the so-called "proved reserves"—some 260 trillion cubic feet—which are the industry's working inventory.) There are several difficulties involved in calculating recoverable supplies. Not the least is the fact that nobody knows the original gas content of present reservoirs, since it was not until twenty years ago or so that natural gas began to be commercially recovered on a major scale. Until then it was considered a nuisance and was vented or burned. But, on the other hand, there is no significant problem of the rate of recovery as there is in crude oil—almost invariably some 80 per cent of the gas in a given field is brought to the surface.

Assumed here are two levels of future recoverable gas: a minimum of 1,200 and a maximum of 1,700 trillion cubic feet, based on recoverable oil and a gas/oil ratio. Aggregate demand between 1960 and 2000 would amount to not quite 1,000 trillion cubic feet—smaller than even the minimum recoverability estimate. However, by the year 2000 annual demand would be running at the rate of 35 trillion cubic feet, and cumulative demand would rapidly be approaching that minimum.

Proved reserves presently amount to about twenty times annual production. If this ratio were maintained through the end of the century, the aggregate 40-year demand would have to be augmented by supporting reserves of nearly another 700 trillion cubic feet, for a total of not quite 1,700 trillion cubic feet. This would exceed by nearly 50 per cent the minimum estimate of recoverability, and just about equal the maximum. Were one to assume that the reserves could be allowed to decline from twenty times production to ten times by the end of the century, then the aggregate demand plus the supporting reserves by the year 2000 would amount to over 1,300 trillion cubic feet. At that level they would exceed the minimum estimate and be rapidly approaching the maximum. Adequacy can thus not be taken for granted. Figure 47 depicts these estimates in simplified form.

Gas imports. At the moment, imports are limited to relatively small pipeline shipments from Canada and Mexico. Canadian imports, which amount to less than 3 per cent of consumption, are bound to increase, but the impact on total U.S. supply is not likely to be very substantial. A second source of imports, so far only potential, is shipment in liquid form. Special tankers have been perfected in recent years, and liquefied methane shipments on a significant scale from the gas fields of Algeria to England are about to begin at an announced price to the distributor of 88 cents per thousand cubic feet—not too different from delivered prices in some parts of the United States.

Commencement of such commercial shipments to Europe undoubtedly will give renewed impetus to earlier proposals in this country to import liquid methane into some U.S. markets near the end of long-distance pipelines, such as New England and perhaps as far down the East Coast as Philadelphia. Under active consideration are liquid gas storage plants in New England designed to assist in meeting peak winter demand that exceeds pipeline capacity. Whether such gas might be shipped through pipelines at off-season periods and then liquefied, or be brought by ships from the Gulf, Venezuela, or even Middle East fields, will be determined by wellhead pricing and transportation cost. Even shipments of liquid methane from Alaskan fields to the West Coast may become competitive.

The gas resources of Venezuela alone could make a sizable contribution to U.S. supplies. In 1958, for instance, 1.7

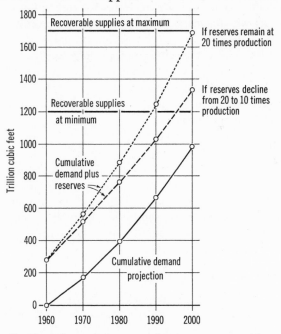

Figure 47. How demand for natural gas compares with estimated recoverable supplies in the United States.

billion cubic feet of gas per day were flared in Venezuela, equal to about 7 per cent of 1960 net marketed production in the United States. Since Venezuelan gas reserves are conservatively estimated at 33 trillion cubic feet, or about one-eighth of proved U.S. reserves, the significance of the liquid methane tanker is obvious.

Substitutes for Natural Gas

Theoretically, other hydrocarbons can be sources of gas, through chemical manipulations. Shale and tar sands are potential candidates for supplementing supplies of natural gas, but most effort has been devoted to extracting oil. The outlook for gasification is more promising with coal as a starting material. The two principal obstacles are the high cost of mined coal, and the necessity for upgrading the low-energy gas which emerges at the end of the process. Efforts to overcome the cost obstacle have been primarily in the direction of eliminating the mining step altogether by gasifying the coal underground. Gas so produced has an extremely low energy content—about one-tenth that of natural gas—and would have to undergo radical upgrading before it could pay its way in pipeline transmission.

Barring technical breakthroughs, such as application of nuclear energy to coal in the ground, it is difficult to see synthetic gas competing with natural gas in the next two decades. However, in local situations especially favorable for premium uses, such as residential application, and more generally later in the century, synthetic gas might emerge as an alternative to natural gas, should supplies of the latter from other sources begin to dwindle.

NGL: Natural Gas Liquids

Related to both oil and gas, and extracted in the processing of both, is a group of hydrocarbons generally lumped under the name "natural gas liquids." The lighter fractions (often called liquid petroleum gas or LPG) have obtained increas-

ing importance as chemical raw material. The heavier portions, known as natural gasoline, are blended with gasoline
derived from crude oil. The NGL content of natural gas, its
principal source, is somewhere near 60 barrels per million
cubic feet.

The future recoverability of natural gas liquids is best
estimated by tying it to natural gas availability, and assuming
an increase in the rate at which the lighter fractions are
recovered. The demand of some 30 billion barrels for the
forty-year period—based on its use as fuel and chemical raw
material—is then found to be confronted by an estimated
recoverability that ranges from 60 to 85 billion barrels.

Thus there is a suggestion of greater ease in supply of NGL
than of either crude oil or natural gas. The projections suggest
that availability of natural gas liquid might to some extent,
and for some time, mitigate any emerging tightness in crude
oil, especially since gas-derived gasoline meets the same demands as oil-derived gasoline. But in the total energy picture
the significance of natural gas liquids lies perhaps more in
affording an additional, profitable outlet than in meeting any
significant portion of the nation's energy needs.

Hydroelectric Power

There is no demand for hydroelectric power as such—only
for electricity regardless of its source. Thus the demand for
hydroelectric power is simply the volume of power to be
obtained from the feasible development of hydroelectric sites
in the next forty years. Assumed by the year 2000 is an installed capacity of 90 million kilowatts—equivalent to exploiting about 70 per cent of what the Federal Power Commission
considers to be the country's total potential hydro capacity,
outside Alaska and Hawaii.

Such a program would by the year 2000 meet about 7.5
per cent of total electricity demand, down from nearly 20
per cent now. Even if all potential hydro sites were developed,
it would contribute barely above 10 per cent. As a share of

all energy—not just electricity alone—hydropower by the end of the century would contribute about 2 per cent.

Atomic Energy

Any attempt to appraise the adequacy of the basic resources of fissionable materials—uranium, thorium, and ultimately perhaps others—encounters almost insuperable difficulties. One can, on the basis of accumulated knowledge, venture an estimate of the amount of coal, oil, or gas needed to produce a kilowatt-hour of energy 20 or 40 years from now. But there is no handy conversion factor relating electric energy to uranium.

U.S. uranium reserves, in terms of U_3O_8, are currently estimated at some 250,000 short tons. This quantity, at present levels of technology, may have an energy equivalent slightly above total U.S. energy consumption in 1960. But with a more highly developed technology, total uranium reserves might be equivalent to 10 times 1960 consumption. At a very advanced technology that would include "breeding" (the production of fissionable materials during generation of electricity), these reserves would be equivalent to perhaps a hundred or more times 1960 energy consumption. It is obviously difficult to strike a balance between these wide-ranging estimates of potentials.

The electricity projection for the year 2000 calls for roughly 2,400 billion kilowatt-hours to be produced in nuclear reactors. For the forty-year period, cumulative power generation in nuclear reactors is projected at about 30,000 billion kilowatt-hours. On the basis of present technology, but allowing for some reduction in the amount of uranium in the supply and distribution pipeline, one can estimate that the amount of uranium needed would run somewhere around 1 million short tons. This would be equivalent to about four times currently estimated U.S. reserves. However, technologists predict unhesitatingly that between now and the end of the century the present energy equivalent of uranium will greatly increase, and that putting it at even twice the current level is a gross underestimation of future possibilities. Such improvements would not, of course, all come at once.

The energy potential of one gram of uranium equals that of 3 tons of coal. At efficiencies obtainable in modern steam electric plants, one gram of uranium is a potential generator of 8,000 to 9,000 kilowatt-hours of electricity. Using this potential as the base, it would take only 4,000 or 5,000 tons of uranium to generate the 30,000 billion kilowatt-hours of electricity projected to be developed by nuclear reactors over the years 1960-2000.

But the full uranium potential is at the end of the line of a technology still in its infancy. Currently estimated reserves of some 250,000 tons would be sufficient for the next forty years only if improvements in efficiency raise energy production per unit of uranium by three or four times above the current level. These comparisons give some idea of the gap between actual and potential. There are also the reserves of thorium, and finally the potential reserves of both uranium and thorium which are now considered too low in quality to be included in the reserves, but which will slowly become commercially useful if the history of other energy sources repeats itself. The development to watch, however, is not the varying estimates of uranium resources, but the advance of reactor technology.

New Technology

Technological advance in the field of energy may take several forms: (1) conventional technology may be applied more efficiently; (2) new types of applications may be devised; (3) new forms of energy conversion may be developed; and (4) new sources of energy may become available. In our projections we have tried to provide for the first through the simple computational device of assuming a continuous decline in input/output ratios in most energy uses and higher recovery in energy production. But, with the conspicuous exception of allowing for new electricity applications in the home by way of "phantom appliances," no provision is made for any other type of technological progress. The need for quantitative expression has barred such attempts.

Actually, even the first category has received attention only in a very general sense. For example, in the field of transportation it has been assumed that miles per gallon of fuel will remain constant. But what if the turbine car should prove to be a success? Or the multifuel engine? Or a new variety that abandons the traditional crankshaft? Presumably, efficiencies would change, and so would the demand for both the type and the volume of fuel. But the effect of these changes would be far from dramatic. Oil would remain the source of energy.

Of greater impact would be changes in the second category, above all because new applications would create demand rather than represent variations of existing arrangements. Which is precisely why they are so elusive. Among them would be such possibilities as electrification of surface transport, an event that would greatly shift the relative demand for the primary energy sources, especially if it were to extend to passenger vehicles.

New energy conversion methods. The third and fourth categories are sometimes confused; and sometimes there are true borderline cases. Of the latter, the fuel cell is a good example. This is a device which utilizes the interaction of gases to generate electricity directly, with high theoretical efficiency. Whereas in steam turbines only 30 to 40 per cent of the energy inherent in the fuel is recovered in the electricity generated, conversions as high as 80 per cent have already been achieved experimentally and are regarded as obtainable in the fuel cell in the next two decades.

Interest in the fuel cell has been growing, but it is too early to gauge either the probability of technical success or the approximate cost of electricity produced in this way. The cost of hydrogen, one of the gases usually involved, is high. If natural gas, oil, or coal should turn out to be an acceptable source, the impact on energy resources would still be mostly through the higher efficiency of the fuel cell rather than through a new source replacing conventional fuels. But if unconventional materials were to supply the gas, one would have to consider the fuel cell as a new source of energy.

Similarly, a rechargeable battery as a source of motive power would increase the demand for electricity and, depending on how this electricity was generated, shuffle the relative importance of the different energy sources. Employing nickel, silver, cadmium, and other metals rather than lead, such batteries may achieve increasing prominence, although their bulk, cost, and limited range between recharges circumscribe their usefulness for general transportation use. Significant progress in improving this type of energy source, as well as the cordless appliance, may in time make its impact on conventional energy sources and strengthen the principal fuels that generate electricity—coal and gas—at the expense of liquid fuels.

Two promising methods, applicable for the time being only on a small scale, are thermoelectric and thermionic conversion. Thermoelectricity, generated by the heating of two types of metals joined together, requires fuel to supply the heat. The efficiency is low, but the operation is simple, and will probably find increasing use in small capacity installations, and may eventually be a good source of power supply in vehicles of limited range. Thermionics, a related method, is more promising as a cooling or heating device than as a means of generating electricity. In this technique, electric energy is used to cool or heat without the intervention of a compressor or motor. Since electricity is initially needed, it is again obvious that thermionics is no new source of energy.

Magnetohydrodynamics—usually called MHD—is a way of improving the efficiency of large-scale electricity generation without the steam cycle. It consists essentially in passing a high velocity gas through a strong magnetic field. Since no steam boiler or turbine is necessary, a high efficiency can be reached—up to 60 per cent. Both fuel and water savings would result. Those close to the research in this field estimate that design of sufficiently heat-resistant materials will permit MHD to pass from the experimental to the commercially feasible stage in no less than ten and no more than twenty years.

Fission, fusion, and beyond. Generation of electricity through nuclear fission is only the most commercially advanced major use of atomic energy. Nuclear-generated heat holds much promise as a substitute for fuel-generated heat in industrial processes, provided it can be made available on a sufficiently small scale to be practical for most of U.S. industry. At the moment, the chances of this seem quite small, but attention may turn to nuclear heat, once nuclear power has become more widely accepted.

Similarly, the application of atomic energy to transportation has lagged behind earlier expectations. In land-borne vehicles the size of the engine, the problem of waste disposal, and the hazard of a moving source of radiation in densely populated areas are formidable obstacles. Nuclear propulsion of ships has progressed more rapidly, especially for navy ships. Once the lessons learned during the first stage of construction and operation are applied, one might expect an accelerated pace. The nuclear plane is still on the drawing board; while the idea is exciting, the effect on energy consumption would naturally be quite small. Complete nuclear ship propulsion by the end of the century would affect no more than 5 per cent of oil demand; nuclear air transport another 1.5. Only a nuclear "battery" or generator (using an isotopic energy source), designed for automobiles, would upset the fuel market, but such a development lies in the distant future.

Nuclear energy has also been eyed as a means of achieving cheap and deep explosions that might help recover petroleum from underground formations not producible by ordinary means, or as a shortcut to recover shale oil by liquefying it in the formations themselves. Thought has also been given to using underground explosions for making available the geothermal heat under the earth's crust. Water would be allowed to percolate through the crushed rock down to the hot zone, where steam would be generated and brought to the surface through wells drilled for that purpose.

Beyond nuclear fission lie nuclear fusion—harnessing the H-bomb—as well as possible new methods of utilizing solar energy, wind, ocean tides, geothermal energy from hot springs or steam vents. Other possible energy sources are the temperature differences of ocean water at different depths, and micro-organisms—the so-called biological fuel cell.

Fusion and solar energy have received the most consideration—fusion because of the accessibility of the raw material and the absence of radioactive debris, and solar energy because the sun shines everywhere and the equipment, as a producer of heat rather than power, could be cheap and on a small scale. Fusion is still in the laboratory stage, but the payoff in perfecting commercially useful fusion for industry is so high that much progress is likely in the coming decades. In contrast, solar energy will find its application principally in residential use for space and water heating. Solar water heaters are in use in Florida, and there are isolated instances of experimental solar-heated houses. But it is not likely that the remaining forty years of the century will see solar energy significantly affecting the national energy picture.

Energy Outlook

Unless novel sources become reality sooner than anybody thinks, the total energy supply picture will probably look about like this: domestic crude oil supplies adequate until around 1980, with a likely tightening of domestic supplies in the latter half of the century; foreign sources of oil adequate to provide a much larger proportion of crude than is now imported; coal as a comfortable cushion; shale oil as a supplement later in the century; demand for natural gas approaching domestic resource limits well before 2000, but with the safety factor of possible gas imports and the likely emergence of synthetic gas late in the century; more than enough natural gas liquids to meet growing demand, especially as raw material for the chemical industry; hydropower, a declining energy source; nuclear fission, a growing energy source, resting on current U.S. uranium reserves that, with expected improvements in reactor efficiency, should see us through to the end of the century and beyond. Again, these are not predictions. They are only projections based on present knowledge and will doubtless be revised many times as the century grows older.

NONFUEL MINERALS

The conditions under which a mineral occurs in nature determine the cost of producing it, and thus its adequacy. This goes for nonfuel as well as fuel minerals. Among the factors that influence cost are the physical and chemical characteristics; the degree of concentration of the material to be mined; the distance from markets, from water sources, from labor supply; the occurrence of a mineral alone or in combination with other valuable minerals; and, particularly in locations outside the United States, the general degree of economic and political stability. There is an infinite number of combinations in which these factors may occur; together they will determine the cost of production.

Physical presence is only the first precondition of exploitation, not the final criterion. Indeed, in physical terms, we are surrounded by an abundance of minerals. Aluminum constitutes 8 per cent of average crustal rock, iron 5 per cent, and so on, down the line to lead, which represents only .002 of 1 per cent of the earth's crust. In the past, we have searched for deposits with high concentrations that could be exploited economically without the need for moving vast amounts of material and separating out a large variety of minerals. Undoubtedly this will remain the pattern for a long time to come. Today, some 500 million tons of material must be handled to produce the major domestic metals; some 10 billion tons might have to be moved if we wanted to recover our metal needs from average rock. Because such great masses of minerals are contained in the crust of the earth, scarcity and depletion are less physical concepts than economic ones. Thus when one speaks of increasing scarcity, one refers properly not to an absolute "running out" of materials as such, but of materials possessing characteristics that enable them to be sold at a price that will attract buyers. And even this is a simplification; for some buyers will continue to be attracted even at the increased price, caused by the deterioration in the characteristics of the deposits; others will turn toward substitute materials. Actually, there is no case in history in which a material has run out, except in a given location. And even in such ancient places as King Solomon's copper mines in Southern Israel or the Cornish tin mines in Britain, changed conditions have revived or are reviving interest in mining operations.

Generally, advancing technology creates new reserves by lowering the cost of exploiting less attractive deposits, or by adjusting fabricating processes so as to enable customers to accept materials of somewhat different composition or properties. The mining of lower and lower grade copper in the United States without a significant increase in real cost is an example of the former; the ability of the steel industry to use chromium of a quality that not so long ago was found unacceptable, illustrates the latter.

All indications point to a truly enormous future demand for minerals, both annually and cumulatively. In the past, prices have been subject to wide fluctuations, but for most minerals the general long-run price trend has been stable, and this despite rapidly increasing demand. But is past success in maintaining an adequate current supply at constant real cost relevant in assessing the future? To keep up with a large annual demand, a high productive capacity is required, and this in turn means that there must be a high level of reserves to sustain production. Either additional reserves must be discovered to replace those that are used up in production, or advances in technology must make possible the profitable exploitation of increasing amounts of what now can only be considered as potential ore. Neither the adequacy of future discoveries nor the effect of technology on potential ore can be taken for granted. Increasing knowledge in geology, physics, chemistry, botany, and other pertinent fields makes it likely that a combination of the two forces will keep the cost of most of our minerals from rising, provided conditions are allowed to prevail under which the bulk of the country's needs can be met from the least-cost sources.

Until fairly recently, the growth in U.S. demand for metals was primarily met by increased domestic output, and this is true even now for the bulk of the nonmetallics. Enough was produced of most metals not only to meet domestic needs, but to provide a significant amount of exports. Since the end of World War II, however, there has been rapidly increasing reliance on imports, so that today the United States has become a net importer of the basic metals and their ores. It is probable that we shall become increasingly dependent on imports, while at the same time U.S. demand will be a declining factor in world demand (see Figure 48).

Iron Ore and Its Alloys

Iron ore. By 1960, imports of iron ore accounted for nearly 35 per cent of U.S. consumption, compared to less than 10 per cent a decade earlier. Imported ores have in general superior qualities such as high iron and low silica content, and sometimes physical structure, that tend to reduce processing costs, and thus enable them to overcome transportation disadvantages. Little domestic ore can compete on a qualita-

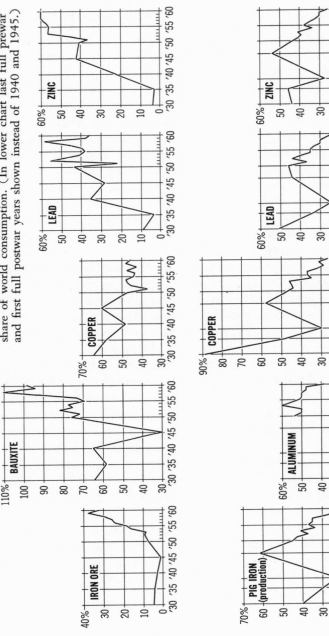

Figure 48. U.S. metals use in a world setting: above, gross imports as a percentage of domestic consumption; below, the U.S. share of world consumption. (In lower chart last full prewar and first full postwar years shown instead of 1940 and 1945.)

tive basis with such foreign ore, unless it is first treated and upgraded into pellets or other types of concentrates so as to raise its iron content to 60 per cent or more.

The outlook for domestic iron ore reserves has changed for the better in the past decade. Increased demand during and after World War II, led to increased domestic production as well as a systematic search for iron ore deposits abroad. And greatly accelerated research at home resulted in domestic low-grade iron-bearing material becoming commercially useful. Now, as the steel industry finds it increasingly advantageous to work with specially prepared ore material, regardless of its original richness, the fact that the domestic grades require preliminary treatment is ceasing to be a disadvantage. All these developments—discovery and exploitation of rich foreign sources, improvement in the handling of low-grade domestic ore, changes in the type of ore most acceptable to the steel industry—have worked to ease the iron ore supply.

As of 1955, the U.S. Geological Survey put domestic reserves of ore at 5.5 billion long tons (equivalent to some 3 billion long tons of iron). Of this, not quite 75 per cent is located in the Lake Superior region. This reserve is about equally divided between the high-grade conventional direct shipping ore and the concentrated material derived from taconite, the low-iron content ore found in the Mesabi and neighboring ranges.

Potential ore (ore not yet commercially useful) was put by the Survey at 65 billion long tons, estimated to contain something like 20 billion tons of iron. By now, a significant part of this potential ore has probably become part of the reserves—how much one cannot tell. The decisive step which will shift the bulk of potential ore into the reserve category will be a commercially feasible way of concentrating the iron that is contained in the nonmagnetic type of taconite, as has already happened with magnetic taconite.

Domestic reserves, as defined in 1955, of 3 billion long tons of iron fall short of equaling the cumulative demand of more than 4 billion long tons. Since one cannot count on all reserves being exploited within the next forty years, the shortfall is actually sharper than is reflected in this comparison of reserves and demand.

The picture becomes much brighter if one looks beyond the reserves that are now commercially exploitable, since much of today's potential ore is likely to become reserves within the next forty years. Total resources (known reserves plus all potential ores for which there are quantitative estimates) of 23 billion long tons of iron-in-ore are equivalent to about 5½ times the cumulative demand between now and 2000. Provided that the remaining technical problems connected with recovering the iron contained in the low-grade U.S. deposits can be solved, there is no question of adequacy, even considering U.S. resources only. Figure 49 compares projected demand with U.S. reserves and resources and with world resources.

It is unlikely, however, that domestic ores will actually be resorted to as the major resource during the next four decades. The discoveries of high-grade foreign deposits in the last ten years have been of such magnitude, and available at such competitive costs, that U.S. consumers are likely for a long time to draw on imports.

Estimated reserves and identified potential ore in non-Communist countries approximate 106 billion long tons of iron, of which not quite half consists of high-grade direct shipping ore. There is reason to believe that this is a conservative estimate, especially with regard to potential ore. For example, this figure includes no potential ore for Africa; yet some have estimated this to range as high as 50 billion long tons, or the equivalent of perhaps 15 to 20 billion long tons of iron.

True, these reserves and resources must supply not only the United States but much of the world. But they are so large that U.S. supply seems assured, irrespective of demand elsewhere. If ore consumption outside the United States were

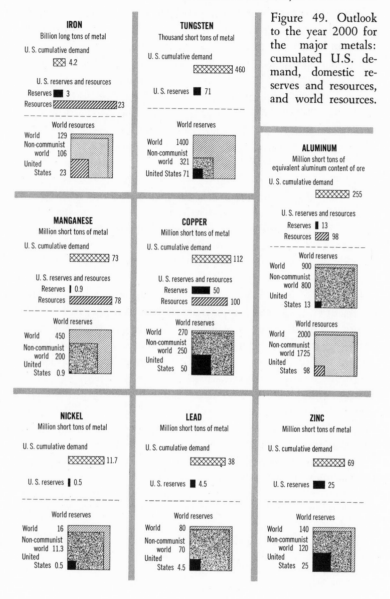

Figure 49. Outlook to the year 2000 for the major metals: cumulated U.S. demand, domestic reserves and resources, and world resources.

to grow at the rate of 5 per cent per year—twice as fast as assumed in the U.S. projections—cumulative consumption in the non-Communist world (excluding the United States) in the four decades would run 16-18 billion long tons of iron-in-ore. Inclusion of U.S. demand, raises this to 20-22 billion long tons. This compares with an estimate of iron in direct shipping ore reserves in non-Communist countries of something like 45 billion long tons, supported by some 65 billion long tons of iron contained in other types of ore, much of it, however, only potential.

Since the iron content in direct shipping ore reserves alone is better than twice the projected level of demand, and since new deposits have been opened up at a rapid rate in the last decade, it should be feasible to mine supplies of the required magnitude without turning to ore that cannot compete without beneficiation of one kind or another. The immediate and perhaps even the medium-term outlook may be characterized as one of abundance, and the long-run outlook as one of adequacy. Aerial mapping and systematic ground reconnaissance have barely begun to be applied on any substantial scale in Asia, Latin America, or Africa. Even closer to home, Canada undoubtedly will yield further surprises numbering in the billions of tons. Thus no concern seems indicated for iron ore supplies for the United States and the rest of the non-Communist world during the next forty years. Indeed, one might easily extend the span of nonconcern substantially into the next century.

The heavy investments made by leading steel companies in foreign countries can be expected to lead to a continued reliance on foreign ore, if for no other reason than to recoup U.S. investments and to utilize foreign sources as long as political conditions permit. At the same time, a domestic industry will be kept in being, shifting generally from direct shipping to beneficiated low-grade ore, but likely to maintain more or less the present aggregate capacity.

Only a breakthrough that would make low-grade domestic ore, derived principally from taconites and similar rock, substantially cheaper than foreign ores, would shift the balance towards domestic supplies. Failing this, the bulk of future increases in consumption is likely to be met from imports. Of the 100 million long tons of iron projected to be consumed in 1980 about one-half might be met from domestic sources, of which one-half, in turn, might be beneficiated ore. By 2000, the proportions are likely to have shifted farther toward imports, which may then fill some 75 per cent of the over 160 million long tons of iron-in-ore projected to be in demand by then. All this presumes, of course, continued access to foreign sources in all parts of the globe, and a commercial policy, both in this country and the exporting countries, that would not discourage trade.

Manganese.   Manganese is a necessary ingredient in making steel, and therefore vital to any industrialized nation. Its main function is to remove impurities, and in the performance of this task it leaves the furnace as part of the slag. The portion that remains in the steel improves its strength and workability. A relatively common metal, it occurs throughout the world in a variety of types of deposit. Like iron, it is mined by a wide range of methods and at many different levels of concentration. This, together with the complex mineralogy of its ore bodies, makes the distinction between reserves and potential ore difficult. A minimum manganese content of 35 per cent is necessary to allow commercial ore to be shipped directly; otherwise, it has to be concentrated from material of lower grade.

The United States has no high-grade deposits. The only presently commercial reserves are in Montana, and are estimated to contain not quite 1 million tons of manganese, testing not much more than 15 per cent on the average. Potential ore of even lower grade is scattered throughout various states, with ore bodies in Minnesota, Maine, South Dakota, and

Arizona, and has an estimated manganese content of some 77 million tons.

Reserves are a drop in the bucket compared with the cumulative demand of 73 million tons. Ore all the way down to a grade of 5 per cent would have to be processed in order to match the projected demand. Unless a way is found to utilize the potential ore without a radical increase in price, the United States must continue to rely on imports. (See Figure 49.)

Why, then, do statistics show that recently the equivalent of as much as 22 per cent of U.S. consumption has been domestically produced? The answer is that these figures are misleading, since most domestic ore was mined under a special government incentive program, at very high prices, and ended up not in commercial use but in the government stockpile.

Potential ore is undoubtedly abundant. Low-grade manganese deposits in the United States, as stated above, amount to nearly 80 million tons, and there are even larger deposits in various parts of the world. In addition, there is the potential afforded by the sea. The existence of manganese-bearing nodules on the ocean floor has been known for many decades, but only in the past few years have investigators begun to glimpse their extent and quantity. They are found at depths varying from 500 to 3,000 feet off the U.S. southeastern coast, and between 5,000 and 14,000 feet in the eastern half of the Pacific.

The size of ocean deposits is startling. At 5 pounds per square foot—a concentration that has been identified in several areas—one square mile of ocean floor would contain 70,000 tons of nodules, equal to no less than 20,000 and perhaps as much as 35,000 tons of manganese. The main deterrent to production is the technique of bringing the material to the surface. Economic production would require a very high volume, perhaps 5,000 tons a day. Considerable risk would be involved in view of the large investment required, as total U.S. consumption at present amounts only to some 8,000 tons of manganese ore a day. Two such sea mines would more than meet U.S. requirements.

Foreign deposits are of key importance. According to the best current estimate, which is a conservative one, there are some 450 million tons of contained manganese in major deposits around the globe, but of these no more than 185 million tons are located in non-Communist countries, principally in Africa and India. In addition, dozens of countries throughout the world produce manganese ore or manganese concentrates from smaller deposits. For example, in 1960 the few non-Communist countries that have major deposits produced 4.5 million tons of manganese ore, while all other countries outside the Communist bloc—whose reserves remain unrecorded—produced another 2.5 million tons.

Since more than half of the large deposits are in Communist territory, the foreign supply base is narrower than would at first appear. Based on future steel production, demand in non-Communist countries in the next four decades may be put at about 300 million tons, which includes U.S. demand of 73 million tons. Comparison with reserves of 185 million tons then suggests a tight situation.

But reserve estimates, as has been seen, are conservative and incomplete. Also, access to the reserves of the Communist countries cannot be considered as barred for the entire next forty years. In fact, from time to time the inflow has been of such magnitude as to provoke demands for its reduction or halt. If Soviet-controlled manganese does not reach the United States directly, it will in all probability reach other parts of the non-Communist world, and thus ease the situation. Moreover, there are indications that the ratio of manganese use in steelmaking is higher than it need be, which, creates a field for technological advance. Then there is the potential secondary source of manganese in slag. For every ingot ton of steel, over 12 pounds of manganese are wasted on the slag dump—only a little less than the total amount added in making a ton of steel. Steel mills are generally careful to segregate their slag and prevent its deterioration, mindful of its possible exploitation eventually. Thus there are several escapes from a tight situation, should the need warrant.

Chromium and Nickel. Apart from manganese, which occupies a special role as a purifying agent in steel production, the largest tonnage items among the metals added to give special properties to steel are chromium and nickel. The domestic reserve situation is not quite as tight for these metals as for manganese. But domestic reserves are not sufficiently large, nor future discovery sufficiently likely, to fill more than a small fraction of domestic consumption. Here, as in manganese, adequacy of resource is dependent upon the situation abroad. This has recently been brought home to everyone by the question of the availability of Cuban deposits, which are among the most extensive low-grade ore bodies in the world.

—Chromium. As with manganese, the statistics of domestic chromium production are misleading. The tenfold increase in domestic output in the 1950's was due to large-scale government subsidies and stockpiling, and is no indication of commercially feasible production. When the government purchase program was ended in 1958, all but one of the domestic mines shut down; the remaining one at Nye, Montana, delivers all its output to the government under a long-term contract.

Domestic reserves are estimated at 4 million tons of chromic oxide—the unit in which chromium is usually measured and traded. The Montana field, which contains the bulk of U.S. deposits, is likely to hold much more than this estimated tonnage. But only a few thousand tons are suitable for use by the steel industry. The U.S. ores are low in chromium content, and are difficult to concentrate. This makes the material undesirable for metallurgical use, even though the steel industry has in recent years been able to adjust its operations so as to use a few thousand tons a year of the domestic ores. Domestic reserves, then, must be considered potential ore, available only under conditions of much higher chromium prices such as prevailed in some past years.

Demand must thus be met predominantly from foreign sources. Of these, the most important are in South Africa and Southern Rhodesia, Turkey, and the Philippines. There are also sizable reserves in New Caledonia, but quantity data on these are not available. Also, both on the supply and demand side, China and the Soviet bloc other than Cuba are excluded, since no data are available. A figure of 500 million tons of chromic oxide as the sum total of chromium reserves in the world, including Cuba, and perhaps 50 million tons less, excluding Cuba, will do for a comparison with estimated demand over the next forty years.

U.S. consumption of chromium has in recent years ranged between ½ million and 1 million tons, fluctuating with steel output. Domestic cumulative demand for all uses is projected at a little over 40 million tons of chromic oxide, and a rough guess at cumulative demand elsewhere would be 160 million tons. Altogether, then, the non-Communist world faces a cumulative demand over the next forty years of about 200 million tons.

Comparison with reserves leaves one in a twilight zone, for judgment of adequacy depends on imprecise factors. Estimates of African reserves range from 250 million to over 1,000 million tons. Just how large are they? What is the extent, nature, and workability of potential ores, other than those known to exist in Cuba? To what degree can grade specifications be relaxed in the future? An additional difficulty arises from the fact that at least half the demand is for metallurgical uses, but only a minor portion of the reserves is now satisfactory for that application.

Since the United States is almost totally dependent on foreign supplies available only via a long sea route, and from areas that may be subject to periods of political instability, the development of Western Hemisphere resources is a matter of special interest. There is no indication of large deposits, however, outside those of Cuba, and the low-grade Cuban chromium is of little value, political considerations apart, until a way is found to produce it at competitive prices.

In summary, qualified concern seems to be in order—not immediately, but somewhere between now and 2000—and technological advance is of great importance.

—*Nickel.* The United States is almost completely dependent on foreign supplies for nickel, as well as chromium. However, the largest reserves of nickel are located within easy and secure reach of the United States, in Canada. The Canadian deposits are rich sulphite ore in which nickel, copper, platinum, and other metals are combined in a way that allows easy separation and utilization of each. The second commercial source is New Caledonia, where nickel is extracted from silicate ores that are low in iron and chromite. With few exceptions, other occurrences of nickel ore are in nickel-bearing iron ores, the so-called laterites, which are found in Cuba, the Philippines, and Indonesia, and which may exist in New Guinea. Canadian and New Caledonian reserves, plus Cuban reserves that are at present minable, add up to no more than 16 million tons of nickel content.

On the other side of the ledger are projected U.S. nickel demand over the next forty years of about 12 million tons and nickel demand in the rest of the non-Communist world of no less than 25 million tons, assuming growth in nickel consumption abroad at some 6 per cent per year. The joint demand is more than double the size of a conservative estimate of reserves, and the discrepancies are even larger if we eliminate Cuban reserves from the picture. Appraisal of the potential ore—which may easily amount to twice as much again as the reserves—is critical in any judgment of adequacy.

Large amounts of low-grade Cuban material have been successfully mined and sold profitably in the United States market without a price incentive or subsidy, despite an ore royalty, the magnitude of which was long a matter of controversy. This experience suggests that technical obstacles do not block the exploitation of low-grade nickel ore. There is reason to believe that, had it not been for the Castro take-over, successful separation and disposition of the other constituents of the ore—cobalt and iron—would not have been far off. This would have been a further step in making the low-grade ores economically attractive.

Unfortunately, there is very little material at hand to judge the cost involved in mining potential ore, the nickel content of which is conservatively estimated at 30-35 million tons. To make up the deficiency of reserves, enough potential ore to yield 20 million tons of nickel would have to be assumed to be economically minable in the next forty years.

Since one-third of the reserves and two-thirds of the potential ore consist of low-grade deposits in Cuba, adequacy of nickel either for the United States or the rest of the world in the coming decades cannot be taken for granted. However, world reserve estimates undoubtedly represent a minimum figure, certainly in Canada where reserve estimates are essentially working inventories and reserves are apt to grow rather than dwindle with production.

With the future of Cuban production in doubt, and little to go on except past success in the continuing expansion of Canadian deposits, satisfaction of demand in the closing decade of the century might have to depend upon a transition to exploiting ores in semitropical or tropical locations such as Indonesia, the Philippines, and throughout the Caribbean. These may hold 10-20 million tons of nickel. However, in many instances distance from U.S. refining facilities would present difficulties. To lower transport costs the entire process from mining to refining may have to be carried on in the country where the ore is mined, and supply problems of fuel, chemicals, etc., would then have to be solved.

In summary, three conclusions emerge: estimated reserves, even if fully exploitable in the next forty years, are insufficient to meet projected demand; past production and the history of nickel reserve estimates suggest that reserves are substantially larger than recorded; and a meaningful appraisal of the contribution that could be made by potential ores will have to wait upon the availability of cost data.

Tungsten. Continental United States contains substantial deposits of tungsten, a metal with a wide range of uses. It serves as a steel additive imparting great hardness and resistance to heat, it finds important use in electric and electronic components, and, as tungsten carbide, it provides shaping and cutting ability in tools. But domestic tungsten consists mostly of low-grade, high-cost material. The extent of commercial exploitation depends entirely on the price level, except where tungsten is produced as a by-product or co-product of some other metal, principally molybdenum.

In the first half of the 1950's, when the U.S. government paid over $60 per short ton unit of tungsten (a commercial measure equivalent to just below 16 pounds of tungsten metal), as much as 7,000 short tons were produced per year at domestic mines. By 1958, a year after the program of incentive prices had terminated, the price had dropped below $20; domestic production had declined to less than 2,000 tons, and the number of mines had dropped from 700 to 2.

It is difficult to say what the reserves are and what the production capacity is. The one available estimate of reserves, dated 1957, indicates 71,000 tons of tungsten metal, but fails to specify at what price level this estimate becomes operative. Since the domestic incentive program ended, only an undetermined and probably very small part of these deposits could be properly termed reserves.

The forty-year demand in the United States has been projected as 460,000 tons of metal, which is more than six times these "reserves." At the 1960 level of domestic consumption of 5,000 tons of metal, this ore would be equivalent to four-teen years of production. It is clear that the United States, while attempting to improve the conditions under which domestic material can be used, must look beyond its borders for its tungsten supplies. (Figure 49.)

No more than 20 per cent of the world's estimated tungsten reserves of 1.4 million tons are located in non-Communist countries. Over 1 million tons are located in mainland China and additional amounts in North Korea and the Soviet Union. Occurrences in some of the other countries including Bolivia, Malaysia, and Burma are available at low prices, and thus constitute proper reserves, but many of the reserve estimates for these areas are twenty years or more out of date. In other areas, as in the United States, reserves listed as such may be available only at elevated prices. On the whole, lack of current data and the severe price fluctuations that tungsten has under-gone make it difficult to secure a realistic picture of reserves in the 1960's.

If consumption in the non-Communist areas outside the United States grows at the same rate as U.S. consumption over the next forty years, total demand cumulated for the four decades might be as high as 1 million tons, or better than three times the 320,000 tons of estimated reserves in the non-Communist world. In addition, a portion of these reserves would probably not be produced without substantially higher prices than are paid today. Little is known about potential ore. In the United States, it is believed, potential ore amounts to about half as much again as reserves, but at what price exploitation would be feasible is not known.

On the optimistic side, there has been a steady increase in the estimated reserves. In 1952, the Paley Commission said, "The future supply of tungsten in the free world may well be inadequate during the next 25 years." At that time non-Communist reserves were put at 270,000 tons, or some 20 per cent lower than now. In the following ten years, world production totaled some 350,000 tons of contained metal, including China and the U.S.S.R., or 200,000 tons excluding these two Communist areas. It would seem, then, that all but 70,000 tons of the reserves have been used up. But to make the current estimate of reserves 320,000 tons, an additional 250,000 tons of new reserves must have come into being. It is this kind of experience that makes one hesitate to speculate another twenty or forty years ahead, especially on the basis of such poor data.

In summary, major discoveries of tungsten ore or large-scale substitution of other metals, such as molybdenum, may have to take place long before the end of the century. But if the data available are as poor a guide to the future today as they were ten years ago, this judgment may be revised before long.

Other ferroalloys. Adequacy of the remaining three ferro-alloys for which demand projections have been made—molybdenum, vanadium, and cobalt—differs radically from the metals considered above. All three appear to be available in large quantities, the first two in the United States, and cobalt abroad. Moreover, estimates of their occurrence have been rapidly adjusted upward in the last few years. All three metals, when added to steel, improve it in one or more desirable directions: greater strength, hardness, resistance to corrosion, abrasion, high temperatures, etc. In most instances, they, as well as the other ferroalloys are used jointly in varying proportions to produce the desired complex of properties. The resulting family of alloy steels consists of so many hundreds of combinations that a four- or five-digit code is used to identify the different kinds. While the list has been growing, to meet new and stricter specifications, there is, on the other hand, much room for substitution. In time of emergency, for example, the aim of maximum serviceability at least cost may give way to maximum use of domestic materials. Thus, prospective inadequacy of any one alloying substance—and this applies to chromium and nickel, as well—must be viewed against the background of substitutability.

—*Molybdenum.* Unlike most other metals, molybdenum is for all practical purposes a U.S. monopoly. For once, comparison of domestic availability with domestic demand is meaningful. The United States has been and will undoubtedly continue to be a net exporter. Cumulative demand over the next forty years exceeds 5 billion pounds. If molybdenum adequacy is ever to become an issue, this will not be until well into the last part of the century.

The most recent world reserve estimate of 4 billion pounds seems conservative. U.S. deposits alone have been estimated to contain at least 3 billion, of which one-third is contained in Western copper-bearing ores. Copper deposits in Chile may include a molybdenum reserve of 1 to 2 billion pounds; those in Canada another ½ billion. Thus the world total may be closer to 6 billion than to 4 billion pounds. In addition, the second largest domestic producer announced late in 1960 that deposits had been located in New Mexico and were estimated to contain nearly 800 million pounds of metal, with investigations not concluded. U.S. domestic and export demand of close to 6 billion pounds may therefore be equaled by reserves now in sight. There is reason to believe that these estimates of reserves are backed up by unknown amounts of poorer materials.

—*Cobalt.* At present cobalt is being consumed in the United States at the rate of some 4,000 to 5,000 tons, valued at about $15 million, a year. It has a wide spectrum of uses, from a blue pigment for glass or ceramics to animal feeds and cancer treatment. Its main commercial use is as both a ferrous and nonferrous alloy. Resistance to corrosion at high temperatures makes it a desirable element in magnets, missiles, jet engines, gas turbines, motors, generators, and other present and future technical applications.

U.S. resources are small: 43,000 tons of reserves with an additional 107,000 tons of potential ore. These obviously cannot meet a cumulated projected demand over the next forty years of 430,000 tons. Foreign reserves are large but predominantly in areas of political instability or worse. Reserves in the Congo, the area of principal production, where cobalt is a by-product of copper smelting and refining, have been put at 750,000 tons, or close to twice projected U.S. cumulative consumption. The Congo has for some time supplied the major portion of cobalt production in the non-Communist world, which in 1960 totaled some 16,000 tons in terms of metal content. There are an estimated 370,000 tons of cobalt of reasonably commercial quality contained in Cuban deposits, plus another 700,000 tons of low-grade ore. These supplies are likely to affect adequacy in the United States and elsewhere indirectly, if not directly. Other areas known to have cobalt-bearing deposits are the Philippines, New Caledonia, Northern Rhodesia, and Canada, but there is a lack of data on cost. A potential source that could immensely widen the reserve base is the cobalt contained in ocean bottom nodules.

Assuming that the United States will be consuming somewhat more than half the world's cobalt, total cumulative demand in the non-Communist world might aggregate 700,-000 to 800,000 tons in the next forty years. In the light of the unsatisfactory reserve and resource data, the net conclusion is that cobalt consumption for most, if not all, the remaining years of the century is not likely to be held in check by depletion of reserves.

—*Vanadium.* The United States is the largest producer and consumer of vanadium. Its usefulness in high-speed, heat resistant, and other alloy steels has given it a firm place in U.S. metallurgy, and encouragement of uranium production has boosted its availability to a level at which no problem of adequacy is in sight for a long time. The best known source of vanadium is the Colorado Plateau, where it occurs with uranium in sandstones and limestones. Thus the by-product production has in itself been more than enough for domestic needs and has provided a surplus of ore and vanadium products for export.

Estimated reserves in the United States total about 600,000 tons of contained vanadium metal—more than triple the projected forty-year demand. Deposits abroad may contain another 400,000 tons. In addition, very large tonnages may exist in various types of minerals that are not conventional sources. The world seems amply supplied for a long time to come, particularly as specialty alloy steels do not become prominent until a nation has reached an advanced level of industrialization.

The Nonferrous Metals

The five traditional nonferrous metals are copper, aluminum, lead, zinc, and tin. There are also relatively new ones, such as magnesium and titanium, as well as a large variety of minor metals that have recently come into prominence.

Nonferrous metals can be substituted for ferrous metals in some instances and for one another, but the difficulties are greater than those that arise when one ferroalloy is substituted for another. Not only is the degree of design change greater, but there is at least a temporary increase in cost. Adequacy or inadequacy of each of the nonferrous metals is hence more significant than that of any one of the ferroalloys, considered by itself.

Copper. The history of copper ore deposits, both at home and abroad, is one of steadily increasing reserves. But, as in the case of petroleum, reserves fulfill primarily the function of a working inventory. Thus the ratio of copper reserves to current production is low.

Copper is mined in this country at a level of concentration some 150 times the average copper content in the earth's crust. The grade of copper ore mined has constantly declined, but at the same time the price has remained stable. In 1880 the copper ore mined contained on the average 3 per cent of copper; by the beginning of World War I this had declined to 2 per cent; in the first half of the 1950's it had dropped to as low as 0.8 per cent. In other words, by the time World War II was past, 4 tons of copper-bearing ore had to be moved for every ton seventy years previously, but additional costs were apparently offset by improved techniques.

Cumulative U.S. consumption of copper in the next forty years has been projected at 112 million tons. This cannot be met from domestic reserves, which have been officially estimated at 32.5 million tons. A more generous estimate, including a guess for inferred reserves, may allow reserves to be set as high as 50 million tons. But that is still not enough. We must increasingly look to the rest of the world, which even now supplies some 30 per cent of the copper ore that is refined (though not all consumed) in the United States.

The latest (1958) count of reserves for non-Communist countries other than the United States stands at 122 million tons (excluding inferred reserves). A more generous estimate by experts of the U.S. Geological Survey in 1952 hazarded a guess at inferred reserves, and came up with a total of 175 million tons. With the discoveries since made, total foreign reserves can be reasonably put at a minimum of 200 million tons. If one included deposits down to an average content of say 1 per cent—still a better grade of ore than the average worked in the United States—foreign copper might easily total 400 or 500 million tons of metal content. For copper, as for other minerals, reserves are only that part of the iceberg which shows. (See Figure 49.)

Foreign reserves are obviously large enough to meet U.S. demand for several decades without regard to the rest of the world. But being more realistic and providing for demand outside the United States at an annual increment of 5 per cent—a rise that appears to have prevailed since 1954—one would have to put cumulative demand in non-Communist countries at some 400 to 500 million tons, which is at least twice the estimated foreign reserves. Even if lower rates of growth in foreign demand prevailed, the working of low-grade deposits would be required to assure a supply/demand balance through the end of the century. However, if U.S. experience is any guide, the high cutoff point in grade now prevailing in most foreign operations can probably be drastically lowered over time without cost increase.

Aluminum. Abundance seems the prospect for bauxite and other ores that contain aluminum, since this is the metallic element that bulks largest in the earth's crust—some 8 per cent of the total. As the specifications for aluminum-bearing material have been lowered, reserves have grown enormously.

Ores are processed successfully today that only twenty years ago would have been considered useless soil. The required content of alumina (aluminum oxide, of which roughly 2 units are needed for 1 of aluminum) has declined from an average of 60 per cent in 1930 to 50 per cent today. Permissible silica content has risen from less than 8 to more than 15 per cent. At the same time, higher rates of extraction and the lower cost of less selective mining have prevented cost increases.

Reserves have also been expanded by the finding of new deposits. A striking instance of accidental discovery occurred when a landowner in Jamaica, troubled by the low productivity of his soil, sent a sample of it to London for analysis; it was found to contain a high percentage of aluminum. That was in 1942. Today Jamaican deposits are estimated as containing some 600 million short tons of bauxite. These have recently been eclipsed by deposits found in Guinea, estimated at 1 billion tons—roughly equivalent to 250 million tons of aluminum.

Demand in the United States alone over the next forty years adds up to about 250 million tons of metal. This compares with U.S. reserves of bauxite equivalent to 13 million tons of metal, and potential ore of about 85 million tons.

As with most other metals, we face the choice between exploiting low-grade materials and importing.

By 1960, imported bauxite going into consumption contributed over four-fifths of total U.S. bauxite consumption, and total imports were nearly equal to consumption, owing to continued purchases for stockpile operations. In addition, this country had a net import balance of finished aluminum, further tipping the scales against self-supply. Much of the aluminum industry is located at the seaboard to receive bulk shipments of foreign bauxite. Since foreign reserves are infinitely larger than domestic, this pattern is likely to persist. At the same time, the large U.S. reserves of low-grade material provide a line of retreat in case of inaccessibility of foreign sources.

The next stage may be a gradual change from importing bauxite to importing alumina or even aluminum. The newly emerging countries are eager to harness their potentially cheap hydropower. In West Africa, in Southeast Asia, and perhaps elsewhere this power could be used to produce aluminum.

Demand outside the United States is likely to grow sharply; even the principal European countries are further behind the starting line and must run faster to catch up. On the assumption that demand outside the United States will grow at a rate 50 per cent higher than that estimated for the United States over the next forty years, the entire non-Communist world would have a cumulative aluminum consumption of some 900 million tons. This is slightly in excess of the 800 million tons of metal in estimated reserves, but only little more than one-half of reserves and identified potential ore jointly (see Figure 49). Moreover, reserve figures are undoubtedly conservative. Australian reserves are anticipated to increase three times present estimates. African reserves will undoubtedly turn out much larger than present estimates, and the U.S. Bureau of Mines doubled its estimate of U.S. reserves between 1950 and 1960. Thus it can be expected that bauxite reserve figures will rise by several billion tons

in the next forty years. In addition, as bauxite occurs predominantly in wet tropical or semitropical regions, it is very
likely that the warm regions of Asia, South America, and
Africa contain unrecorded deposits.

The potential tonnage of low-grade bauxite and bauxitic
clays—characterized by lower content of alumina, higher
content of harmful silica and iron and occurrence in thinner
deposits—runs into the tens of billions of tons. In the last
resort, the clay in our backyards is a potential aluminum
reserve. But the processing of bauxites with a high silica or
iron content and of various nonbauxite aluminum-bearing
minerals should carry us indefinitely.

Much discussed is the direct reduction of aluminum-bearing ore which bypasses the intermediate alumina stage. At
least one U.S. company has announced that it will introduce
this method in its next expansion move. A basic advantage
would be the elimination of a great deal of labor and facilities connected with the initial stage in which bauxite is
processed into alumina. Possibly as much as one-third of
present capital requirements could be saved. Secondly, some
of the processes that bypass the production of alumina could
utilize almost any kind of aluminum-bearing ore. In the long
run, this approach may, therefore, be as successful in widening the industry's already satisfactory raw material base as
continuing attempts to improve the recovery of alumina from
clay.

Lead and zinc. Cumulative demand for lead in the United
States is projected at 38 million tons over the next forty years.
Excluding the Sino-Soviet area, foreign demand for the same
time span, at current consumption levels, would require an
additional 45 million tons. To supply this combined demand
of some 80 million tons there are U.S. reserves of less than
5 million tons, and reserves—measured and indicated only—
in the rest of the non-Communist world of around 33 million
tons. If a guess at inferred reserves is added, total reserves

in the non-Communist world are probably between 70 and 75 million tons, an amount that is still short of the projected demand. (See Figure 49.)

But even this picture is too rosy. The assumption of constant demand abroad is not realistic. Recent experience suggests a growth in the long-run demand rate abroad of 2½ or 3 per cent per year. At such a rate, demand abroad would cumulate to 80 or 90 million tons, not 45 million. Including the United States, total demand would then be 130 million tons, which is almost twice as large as estimated reserves.

Even if the estimate of world reserves of lead is increased to 150 million tons by including a more generous allowance for inferred reserves, supplies would tighten long before the end of the century. With lead, as with other minerals, reserves cannot be expected to be exploited at a steadily rising rate, then followed by sudden exhaustion.

New discovery, above everything else, is the crucial factor in lead. This seems true not only for the United States, but for the world as a whole. New occurrences of lead have been located in eastern Tennessee and in New Brunswick, Canada. The Canadian deposit, unknown at the onset of the 1950's, is estimated to hold close to 3 million tons of lead, which is equal to total current measured and indicated reserves of the entire United States.

The situation of zinc is similar to that of lead, except that zinc reserves are larger in both the United States and the rest of the world. Cumulative domestic demand in the next forty years equals about three times U.S. reserves and about one-half world reserves. As in the case of lead, a balance of reserves and demand in the next forty years is not attainable for either the United States alone or for the non-Communist world as a whole, since 120 million tons of world reserves, excluding Communist areas, are confronted with some 170 million tons of demand.

In order to establish any outlook of adequacy in the next forty years, the 47 million tons of recoverable foreign zinc that are officially carried as existing outside the Sino-Soviet areas would have to be boosted to something like 200 million tons to promise anything like a meeting of projected consumption. This would imply that inferred reserves are at least three times the size of the measured and indicated reserves—a possibility presently without proof. (See Figure 49.)

There are no estimates of potential ore for either lead or zinc. Perhaps little potential ore exists. This explanation could account for what happened during World War II and the Korean conflict when the U.S. government attempted to stimulate the output of lead and zinc by offering a subsidy. Although the subsidy was large in relation to the market price, the resulting increase in production was insufficient for the combined needs of consumption and stockpiling. It is possible that in the case of lead and zinc there is no gradual transition from higher to ever lower grades, as there is in aluminum, copper and iron ore, and that after the ore reaches a certain low-grade level the metal content vanishes. It is also possible that so far there has been little incentive to explore and analyze in environments other than those traditionally connected with lead and zinc mining. No judgment can be rendered at this time.

Tin. Domestic resources of tin are negligible. Interest is therefore focused on the producing areas: the Malayan peninsula, Indonesia, Thailand, Bolivia, the Congo, Burma, in that order of importance, plus a few minor ones. Reserves in these countries have been put at 5 million tons of metal content. This figure was first put forward ten years ago as no more than an approximation based on individual estimates made on varying assumptions as to cost, grade, and other factors. Although supplies equivalent to perhaps 40 per cent of the 5 million tons have been produced since 1950, the old estimate of reserves remains unchanged.

The 5 million tons of reserves compare with an estimated cumulative U.S. consumption of 3 million tons of primary metal for the next forty years, and are equal to about thirty years of consumption by all non-Communist countries at the level prevailing in the 1950's. But considering the principal sources of supply—Malaysia, Indonesia, the Congo, Thailand, and Bolivia—one realizes that problems of political and economic stability loom larger in any appraisal of the future adequacy of tin than does the quality of reserve estimates.

Increased substitution of other materials adds another element of uncertainty. Aluminum has made significant inroads in canning; nonmetallic forms of packaging and conserving may bring about further lowering of demand; and advances in printed electronic circuits as well as spread of nonmetallic piping threaten to hold down the use of solder, tin's second most important market. And production control by countries adhering to the International Tin Agreement affects consumption and price, so that past trends are not necessarily a guide to the future.

The projection of U.S. tin ore requirements for the year 2000 is only a little more than 75 per cent above the 1960 level—one of the lowest demand growth rates for any materials so far considered. Although reserves of tin appear inadequate to meet future demand, cost increases and substitution may add further impetus toward reducing the use of tin.

Magnesium. Magnesium is the light metal *par excellence.* It weighs only 109 pounds per cubic foot, compared with 165 for aluminum, its closest competitor, and 490 for steel. Since sea water is the primary raw material, no resource problem is in sight. A sudden boost in demand might present a processing capacity problem, but even this would not last long.

Our interest in magnesium is therefore more in its competitive impact on other metals, such as aluminum, than in its demand on resources. This impact has been most erratic, not only in the United States but throughout the world.

After World War II and again after the Korean conflict, magnesium production slumped to a fraction of the wartime output. In the last decade production in the United States ranged between 30,000 and 50,000 tons a year, with only the barest indication of an upward trend. Interestingly, from what is known, the Soviet Union, the world's largest producer, seems to have had a similar experience. This may result from a reluctance to tackle some of the characteristics of the metal—among them poor corrosion resistance, high inflammability in processing, and difficulty of producing alloys with improved properties.

Perhaps the best publicized recent peacetime application is in the manufacture of the Volkswagen in West Germany, which uses it in housings, brackets, fittings, covers, and much of the engine block. At similar magesium poundage per automobile in this country, U.S. consumption would be at least 140,000 tons above the 40,000 to 50,000 ton level of the late fifties. This still would not raise magnesium to the level of a major tonnage metal.

Because the raw material is so abundant, no formal projections of magnesium are made. However, should the basic situation change and magnesium catch on at a rising rate, the result would be an easing of the demand for aluminum and, to the extent that materials other than aluminum are replaced, a net increase in the consumption of electricity. Since aluminum and magnesium are about equally heavy consumers of electricity, substitution would affect power consumption only if more than one unit of magnesium were needed to replace one of aluminum.

Titanium. Titanium has had a shorter career than magnesium but an even more erratic one. With its high strength-to-weight ratio and its great resistance to corrosion, titanium seems to combine some of the best characteristics of high-grade steel and aluminum. But difficulties in workability from ore reduction through machining and scrap recovery, have stood in the way of rapid acceptance. Simultaneous improvement in competing materials, notably high-strength steel alloys, has held down its growth.

Fifteen years ago, titanium seemed tailor-made for the space age. Not surprisingly, it received large-scale financial encouragement by government. Hailed as the miracle metal, by 1952 titanium seemed to be heading rapidly into the family of major tonnage metals. Annual consumption of 100,000 tons was freely predicted, and government efforts were bent toward bringing facilities into existence that would produce no less than 35,000 tons per year.

Then the goal was reduced to 22,500 tons. By 1957 the boom that had begun in 1948 was spent. Having risen from 500 tons in 1951 to over 17,000 tons in 1957, production dropped to under 5,000 tons in 1958. Titanium has recovered only slightly since, and, at that, U.S. production represents over half of world output. At least two previous producers have closed shop, and several potential ones never got into operation. Capacity has settled at some 20,000 tons of metal sponge (the stage preceding ingots).

When it first appeared in commercial form in 1948, titanium sponge was priced at nearly $5 per pound. By 1960, the quoted price was $1.60, and the selling price was even lower. Defense is still the principal customer, as large-scale commercial markets have so far failed to materialize. Even now the chemical industry, a large potential civilian consumer, takes only 2 per cent of total titanium purchases, but there is some reason to think that the next generation of jet planes may provide a big boost for non-military use of titanium.

The future of titanium remains in doubt, but at one-third its 1952 price and with a growing demand for specialty materials it cannot be written off. Should titanium ever become a large tonnage metal, availability of raw materials should not be an obstacle. In addition to rutile, which is the more economical, but domestically less plentiful of the two titanium-bearing minerals, there is ilmenite, which occurs in abundance both in the United States and Canada. Ilmenite would have little trouble in constituting satisfactory support for a growing industry.

Minor Metals

There are easily two dozen minor metals in common use—minor, that is, in tonnage or value or both. This is a minimum figure, since all sixteen of the rare earths are counted as a single metal, and the six metals in the platinum group as only one. Many of these metals have short histories; data have not been systematically collected; and most of the trends that might be established are based on unusual and transitory circumstances that are poor guides to the future. Often the value of the minor metals was first recognized for highly specialized military and allied uses, where performance was more important than cost. But their long-run potential rests on civilian uses. Principal present uses of the minor metals are shown in Figure 50.

Resistance to very high temperatures or to corrosion, performance of special functions in electronics or medicine, additives to plastics and ceramics—these are some of the properties and uses that may give the minor metals their ultimate market. Figure 51 shows the properties of the minor metals that are currently most important in their use as metals. Their future rests on new techniques and new ideas which cannot be predicted or projected.

Some metals are minor because only recently has looking for them become worthwhile. Uranium is a good example of a metal that, when recognized, was found in abundance. Others may be minor because they are not found in conventional locations or by conventional techniques; brines instead of rock may turn out to be the "ore." Another reason for limited supply is that a metal may not be concentrated into easily workable deposits. Rubidium, for example, is concentrated barely five times in its major source found so far, whereas a 1 per cent copper deposit represents a concentration

Figure 50. Principal uses of the minor metals and their alloys and compounds.

	Ferrous alloys (steel making)	Electrical industry	Electronics industry	Chemical, rubber and petroleum industry	Food, textiles, other industries	Glass & ceramic industry (incl. refractories)	Paints, pigments and enamels	Structural metal: aircraft	Structural metal: other	Nuclear reactors	Storage batteries	Bearing metal	Soldering, welding and brazing	Machine tools	Control and measuring equipment	Decorative and uses giving special protection	Munitions and explosives	Insecticides and fungicides	Drugs and pharmaceuticals	Other
Antimony				>	✓		✓				✓	✓	>		>	✓	>	✓		
Arsenic			>	>			>										>		>	
Beryllium						>		>	>	>					✓					
Bismuth			>	>	>	>				>	✓	>	>	✓	>	✓			✓	
Cadmium			>			>			>	>		>	>		✓	✓				
Cesium			>		>	✓								>	>					Fuel
Columbium	✓		>			>				>			>		>					
Gallium		>	✓			>									>					
Germanium			>												✓					
Hafnium																				
Indium		>	✓	✓		>	>			✓	>	✓			✓	>			>	Lubricants
Lithium		>		>		>	✓				>	>	>		>	>		>	>	Lamps
Mercury		✓				>											✓		>	Catalyst
Platinum Group		>		✓		>		>	>						>				>	Carbon arcs
Rare earths	>	>		✓	>	✓	✓									✓				
Rhenium			>	>		✓														
Rubidium			>	>		>														
Silicon		✓	✓	>		✓	✓													
Strontium				>		✓	✓								✓					
Tantalum	✓	>	>	>		>	✓							>	✓	>		>		High-speed alloys
Tellurium	✓	>	>	>		>			>					>	>			✓	✓	
Thallium			>	>		>	✓	✓						>	✓			✓	>	Lamps
Titanium	>	>	>	>	>	>									>	>				
Yttrium		>	>																	
Zirconium	>	>	>	>	>	✓			>	>					>	>				

✓ Major uses.

Figure 51. Important properties of the minor metals and their alloys and compounds.

	Low weight	Melting point: high	Melting point: low	High thermal conductivity	Electrical conductivity: high	Electrical conductivity: low	Semi-conductive	Thermoelectric	Other special electrical properties	Good structural properties	Ductile and/or easily worked	Hard or hardener	Low friction coefficient	Reactive	Deoxidizer or reducing agent	Corrosion resistant	Coloring agent	Poisonous	Low neutron cross-section	Radioactive	Other
Antimony			+					+	+			+	+			+	+				Fire resistant +
Arsenic			+			+			+	—	+	+			+	+	+	+			Decolorizer +
Beryllium	+	+		+	+				+	+	—	+				+		+	+		Nonsparking +
Bismuth	—		+	—				+		+	+		+					+	—		
Cadmium			+					+	+	+				+		+	+	+			
Cesium			+																	+	
Columbium		+	+				+		+	+	+	+				+				+	
Gallium			+				+		+							+				+	
Germanium			+				+		+			+				+					
Hafnium		+							+			+		+		+					
Indium			+				+			+			+			+					
Lithium	+		+							+			+	+	+	+				+	Hygroscopic +
Mercury	—		+	—							+	+		—		+		+		+	Luminescent vapor +
Platinum Group		+			+						+			—		+			—		
Rare earths	—	+			+				+	+	+	+		—	+	+					Sparking +
Rhenium	—	+							+	+	+	+				+	+	+			Incandescent +
Rubidium	—	+							+		+									+	Absorbs light +
Selenium							+		+		+			+	+		+	+			
Silicon	+	+					+		+	+		+			+	+	+	+	+		Many variables +
Strontium									+	+					+	+	+				
Tantalum		+					+	+	+	+	+	+				+					
Tellurium							+				+	+				+	+	+	+		Luminescent vapor +
Thallium	—		+			+				+						+		+	+		
Titanium	+	+		—		+			+	+	—	+	—		+	+					
Yttrium	—	+		—						+	—	+			+	+			+ +		Transmits microwaves +
Zirconium		+								+				+	+	+			+		Magnetic +

— Indicates that metal has poor or opposite characteristic for the given property.

of 180 times that of average abundance in the earth's crust, and a 2 per cent lead deposit, which is not uncommon, is 1,300 times the average abundance. In some instances, a desired metal may be won only with great difficulty from the rock which contains it or from sister metals. Beryl, the ore of beryllium, for example, must be separated by hand from associated minerals. Columbium and tantalum, or zirconium and hafnium, are sister metals difficult to separate.

Annual domestic production of minor metals is in a few cases less than one ton, more commonly amounts to a few hundred tons, and rarely is more than 10,000 tons. In most cases, gross weight of ores and concentrates is on the order of 10,000 short tons, leading to much smaller amounts of metal. Value amounts only rarely to as much as $10 million a year. One may roughly estimate that the annual total value of their primary forms—the unfabricated metals themselves, their alloys, and compounds—in recent years has not exceeded $600 million.

There can be no flat answer to the question of whether available supplies of each of the minor metals will be sufficient. However, it can be said that, considering the world as a whole for supply as well as demand, few of these metals seem to be in short supply. Increased demand could lead to price increases, but higher prices would probably not last long. And they would have only a minor effect on the economy as a whole, unlike a long-term cost increase in, say, iron ore, which would permeate the whole economy.

Nonmetallics

The only nonmetallic, nonfuel minerals considered here are sulfur, phosphates, and potash. All three are vital parts of the chemical industry and, together with nitrogen, of fertilizer production. Among the others, some are of small economic importance. Some, like stone, sand, lime, and salt, are so plentiful and so ubiquitous that nobody has ever felt compelled to compile reserve and resource estimates, although there may be supply problems for specific grades or at a given location. Still others, such as quartz and diamonds, are being successfully supplemented or replaced by synthetics.

Sulfur was extremely scarce in the early fifties; distribution was controlled, and the price was high. Today there is an abundance of sulfur, prices have receded, competition is active, and a period of long-term ease seems ahead.

The temporary shortage after World War II led to tapping the sulfur contained in crude oil and natural gas deposits. Its presence and necessary removal had long been a source of annoyance and cost to the refiner or pipeliner. Its recovery was not economically competitive with sulfur produced by the Frasch process, which consists of injecting superheated water into underground sulfur deposits (domes) and pumping the liquefied sulfur to the surface.

In recent years, the expansion of Frasch-type production has halted, and a steep rise has begun in sulfur recovery from oil and gas. Oil and gas production yielded nearly 4 million tons of by-product sulfur in the decade ending in 1960. Annual production is now approaching 1 million tons, and sulfur from oil and gas, recovered in some sixty plants, represents nearly 12 per cent of domestic sulfur production. This changeover to a new source has been accompanied by a decline in the price of sulfur, relative to the general price level.

Estimates of sulfur reserves are highly speculative. Those in underground domes, for example, range from as low as 50 million to as high as 200 million tons. If reserves in U.S. domes are put at 150 million tons, and similar Mexican reserves of some 50 million tons are added, together with 75 million tons recoverable from domestic oil and gas and the very large Canadian ultimate reserves from gas fields of perhaps 260 million tons, the outcome is over 500 million tons of sulfur reserves in the Western Hemisphere, all of them easily accessible to the United States.

Sulfur recovery from gas and oil production in other countries has been on the rise—most spectacularly so in the Lacq natural gas field of southwestern France which now produces over 1 million tons a year. Similar, though smaller, sulfur recovery is being carried on in many countries with oil refineries or gas processing facilities; this trend can be expected to continue. Sulfur from Middle East and Africa oil and gas may yield several hundred million tons over time.

Beyond the subterranean and submarine sulfur domes and the sulfur present in oil and gas lie immense reserves of sulfur-bearing iron pyrites, and sulfur-bearing gypsum and anhydrite. Finally, there are the potential hydrocarbon sources other than crude oil and natural gas. It has been estimated, for instance, that the Athabasca tar sands of Canada contain more than 2 billion tons of sulfur.

Most sulfur is turned into sulfuric acid, which enters as a basic ingredient into so many industrial processes that its statistical behavior has sometimes been used as a gauge of industrial activity as a whole. There is no reason to doubt that projected industrial growth can equally serve as the indicator of demand for sulfur. On that basis, cumulative domestic demand over the next forty years may be estimated at 600 million tons, to which would have to be added at least 75 million tons to maintain traditional sulfur exports. It seems unlikely that such quantities can be satisfied from U.S. reserves as presently identified, though judgment has to be tempered. One of the largest sulfur domes ever to be found was discovered not so long ago 7 miles off the Louisiana coast and 2,000 feet beneath the Gulf floor, and was unofficially estimated to contain 30 to 40 million tons, or several times U.S. annual production. It would not take many such spectacular discoveries to raise domestic reserves to the U.S. demand level. However, developments ouside the United States are likely to continue to be of importance to the United States as well as to the rest of the world.

Fertilizer materials. The future of the three principal plant nutrients—nitrogen, phosphate, and potash—seems to rest on a firm resource basis. The bulk of this country's nitrogen is being synthesized—in the form of anhydrous ammonia—from hydrogen and air. The hydrogen is obtained from either gas or oil, in a variety of chemical processes that make the resulting nitrogen compounds thoroughly competitive with imported material and with coking plant by-products.

As for phosphate, the cumulative call on reserves in the United States, measured in terms of phosphoric oxide (P_2O_5) is probably in the neighborhood of 250 million tons over the next forty years, based on a tripling of annual phosphate consumption over this time span. Providing for phosphate use other than as fertilizer and for continuing exports at current rates adds another 150 million tons or so. Total forty-year demand is equivalent to perhaps 1,100 million tons of rock. No question of depletion arises. Florida alone has about 50 per cent more reserves than necessary to meet this demand, and western reserves in Idaho, Montana, Wyoming, and Utah are estimated at over 2 billion tons. Beyond the reserves are an estimated 12 billion tons of potential rock consisting of lower-grade material, and the prospect of mining phosphorite from the sea bottom.

Potash recoverable reserves in the United States, in terms of K_2O are estimated at 400 million tons, but this takes in only material with at least 14 per cent potash content. If the threshold were lowered to 10 per cent, the size of the reserves would double or better; if lowered to 5 per cent, the fields could be worked for a thousand years at the current rate of production.

Total U.S. reserves, even at a cutoff level of 14 per cent, are nearly double the consumption projected through 2000 for the United States, even assuming a quadrupling aggregate annual consumption between now and the end of the century.

An additional consideration is the truly vast occurrence of potash in Canada, with the almost astronomical figure of 6,400 million short tons of potash content with a minimum grade of no less than 25 per cent. West and East Germany between them are estimated to have deposits four times as large as those reported in Canada. No matter what political constellations may develop, reserves of such magnitude cannot help but assure future supply for the United States.

5

Some Major Issues
of Policy

Comparison of this country's projected resource requirements with the availability of resources to fill them is on the
whole encouraging. There is no reason to expect any widespread scarcity that would raise the real cost of resources and
resource products enough to hamper continued economic
growth in the United States.

But this favorable state of affairs will not come about auto-
matically. It will depend on continuing advances in technology, reasonably open channels of world trade, and adaptation of political and economic patterns to meet changing
conditions. None can be realized without conscious effort. In
addition, there probably will be severe short-term supply
problems for some materials and painful problems of social
adjustment when mining, farming, or some other kind of
resource production shifts out of its traditional area to other
parts of the United States or to some other country. There
will be problems of how to make wise investments in timber
production, water development, and other long-term resource
enterprises. And there will be long-range problems of maintaining or restoring the quality of land and water.

To overcome these varied difficulties the American people
must decide intelligently and then act effectively. The resources outlook presents major policy issues. What can individual Americans do about these issues? Executives in industries that produce or use resource materials will have
special opportunities and responsibilities, as will elected or

appointed public officials who deal with resource problems. Members of private and civic groups will have many chances to study and make up their minds about the particular questions of their communities, especially in land and water use. Much valuable educational work is being done by the League of Women Voters, the U.S. Chamber of Commerce, labor unions, and other volunteer associations. But beyond that, every citizen can be on the watch for state and national issues of natural resources and use them as one of his criteria in voting on candidates, constitutional amendments, or proposed bond issues.

The Continuity of Resource Policy

In considering the most urgent policy implications of our study it is important to remember that future decisions will not be written on an entirely clean slate. Just as future demand trends grow out of those of the past, future resource policies evolve from past policies.

The First Conservation Movement, which reached its peak in the administration of Theodore Roosevelt, grew out of recognition that the geographic frontier period was about over, that tendencies toward monopolistic control of certain basic resources needed curbing, and that large advantages could be secured through development of resources for multiple purposes. Policy objectives conceived during this period, however vague, did guide and shape specific policies in regard to forests, water, oil, and other resources.

The Great Depression of the 1930's gave rise to new policies and policy objectives in the resource field. The shoring up of incomes in agriculture and the stimulation of the economy through programs of public works, many of them resources projects, became of central importance. The Tennessee Valley Authority was created. Dust storms on the Great Plains and the growing awareness of water erosion led to soil conservation activities on a large scale.

The Second World War and the re-establishment of the economies of the Western European countries after the war placed heavy demands on raw materials, demands that continued during the cold war and Korean War that followed. Population growth spurted during the latter half of the 1940's. This country became more dependent on imports of oil, iron ore, and many other metals. A huge stockpiling program, mainly for metals, was undertaken against the possibility of a protracted war. Economic growth was given increasing emphasis as an objective of national policy. In the resource field, for the most part, policies were confined to modifications and extensions of the policy innovations of the 1930's.

The new role of the United States in world affairs, the need for helping countries ravaged by the war, its longer-term responsibility for aiding less developed areas, an increasingly marked net import position for important raw materials, new and uncertain defense requirements, and an urgent need to maintain a stable and growing domestic economy called for major shifts in objectives of resource development and for major policy responses. A number of notable studies of the impact of these changes, such as that of the President's Materials Policy Commission, were made in the postwar period, each in its field attempting to state the problems and recommend more comprehensive and consistent public policies. These recommendations, however, have not thus far called forth great response from policy makers.

Agricultural policies continue to be characterized by price supports and surplus stocks, acreage controls and fertilizer payments, soil banks and subsidized irrigation—all underscoring stubborn inconsistencies. Water resource policies and administration remain in a tangled condition with rival claimants, purposes, and agencies competing for position. In the face of some real difficulties, mineral industries seek tariff protection and favored tax treatment—and government seeks to aid exploration in the search for greater self-sufficiency— while comparative cost trends and the need of less developed countries to export raw materials inexorably lead this country to import more and more.

Clearly there is need for resource policies that are more consistent with each other and in better harmony with the broader policies of domestic economic growth, foreign relations, and defense. Such remolded resource policies would recognize the need for multiple-purpose management—frequently on a regional basis going beyond state lines; efficient production and use of land, water, and mineral resources; wide diffusion of benefits from resource development projects with equitable sharing of costs; and adequate consideration for the qualitative, more or less nonmonetary, aspects of resources such as clean air and unspoiled scenery. The ultimate objectives of new resource policies would, of course, be their sustained contribution to economic growth and stability in this country and elsewhere, a strong national defense, and progress toward world peace.

Some Major Problems in Brief

With this background in mind, let us take a brief look at a few of the most troublesome resource problems suggested by this study. Each of them will call for policy decisions.

We shall not consider population among the major issues, although the number of people to be served is fundamental to all questions of resource adequacy. Instead, we take people as one of the "given" elements in the equation, using the best available estimates of future population. To do otherwise would be to lose the whole point of our inquiry, which is whether there can be enough resources and resource products for a growing population. Furthermore, many of the people who will live in the United States between now and the year 2000 already have been born, and it is unlikely that conscious national decisions in the next four decades would significantly affect the birth rate. Finally, there is nothing in the economic outlook for the rest of the century (or for a long time thereafter, if a broad impression may serve in the absence of detailed analysis) to suggest that the U.S. population will put enough pressure on resource supplies to impede economic growth. Eventually it may well be that for other reasons—dislike of crowded living or families' desire to provide better education to fewer children, for example—the nation's population will grow much more slowly than in recent years, or even decline.

Research, development, and investment. At many points in this study the need for continued gains in technology stands out clearly; without such advances the ever-present tendencies for demand to outrun supply, save at increased cost and prices, cannot be held in check. Yields will have to continue to increase in agriculture. Reuse of water within industries, improvements in pollution treatment, and many other adaptations of new technology—perhaps even the beginning of desalinization—will be called on. Continued advance in techniques of exploration for ores and of their extraction and processing, plus increased efficiency in getting heat and power from fuels, will be necessary to satisfy demands for mineral materials and energy. By the last two decades of the century, nuclear power and liquid oil from shales and tar sands will probably contribute significantly to energy supplies. The main escape hatch from scarcity is technological advance across a broad front, and behind this have to be large, varied, effective programs of research and development in science engineering, economics, and management. And to back up these efforts, in turn, there must be a strong system of general education at all levels.

Total research and development (R & D) expenditures in 1960, governmental and private, were on the order of $12 to $15 billion, of which upwards of $1¼ billion apparently was in the resources field. R & D expenditures on resources will have to increase greatly in the future if an ample flow of low-cost materials is to be continuously available and if the resource base is to be maintained and utilized effectively. A doubling of expenditures for resources research and development in each of the next two decades would lift the total to $5 or $6 billion by 1980, which would come to about one-half of 1 per cent of projected gross national product.

Also, expanded programs of investment in resource conservation and development will be needed along many lines if projected demands are to be met. Omitting operation and maintenance expenditures, government investments in resources in 1960 were probably around $5 or $6 billion. Somewhat less than half of this total was by the federal government; the larger portion of the remainder was for local water and sewage works. Perhaps $3 or $4 billion was invested privately, mostly by the oil and gas industry. Thus total annual investments for resources were in the neighborhood of $9 billion in 1960, nearly 1.8 per cent of gross national product in that year. If 2 per cent of GNP was invested in resources by 1980, the total would come to about $22 billion, an increase of two and one-half times over 1960.

These sums may seem staggering, but it is clear that if the levels of demand projected in this book are to be satisfied, with allowance at the same time for improvements in the condition of the resource base of land and water, a considerable over-all increase in capital outlays for resources will be necessary. They are the means for translating research and development findings into practical applications. Any serious diminution or delay of investment in these lines will undercut one of the foundations of the economy.

A reasonably free world trading system. The United States already leans heavily on imports of numerous commodities which are vital to its economic growth and national defense; for about three decades it has been a net importer of resource materials. By 1948 the United States for the first time became a net importer of oil, and shortly afterwards of iron ore. It is clear that in the future even larger amounts of certain items will have to be drawn from foreign sources if demand is to be satisfied without marked increases in cost. On the other hand, the United States remains a large net exporter of a number of basic agricultural crops, notably wheat, cotton, and feed grains. If the world trading system should deteriorate so that less goods were traded internationally, U.S. supply problems in minerals and its market problems in agriculture would be intensified.

American policy for mineral fuels and nonfuel minerals has never been clear as to whether to take full advantage of cheaper and more plentiful sources wherever located, or to favor perpetuation of existing patterns. The objective of obtaining an adequate and dependable flow of raw materials at least cost has general appeal, but it has had to be reconciled with such other considerations as national defense, the position of domestic industries and regions that might be affected by larger imports, and the interests of friendly nations. A lowest-cost policy would mean a considerable increase in imports of oil, as well as other raw materials, and this might not square with the national security objective of minimum dependence on distant sources that might be cut off in time of war. (Some people maintain, however, that larger imports would enhance national security by making it possible to retain more domestic oil in the ground available in time of need. A counter to this argument is that a modern all-out war most likely would be a short one so that underground stocks of oil would be of no benefit.) Further problems arise when the interests of friendly nations are considered. Larger U.S. imports from the Middle East and Venezuela would tend to promote economic development of those areas; on the other hand, a large domestic U.S. capacity in oil production and refining is important to Western Europe in case countries there should be denied access to oil from their principal sources of supply in the Middle East. Similar considerations bear on imports of lead and zinc, iron ore, and many other minerals.

It will be hard to reconcile these general objectives, and even harder to translate objectives into specific policies. But U.S. policy on imports and treatment of foreign investments must strike its compromises with the conflicting alternatives clearly in view.

Multiple use of the nation's land space. Increasing demands on land space for outdoor recreation, urban growth, highways, airports, and perhaps forests by the year 2000 will far exceed any relief provided by possible reduction in land needed for crops and the amounts of now unused land that can be pressed into service. According to the estimates for 2000, land requirements, if each use is counted separately, would add up to 50 million more acres than the country has, and this assumes no increase whatsoever in forest land. There are two ways to avoid so untenable a situation: more intensive single-purpose use of land, and multiple-purpose use of land. The second alternative offers new and expanded opportunities for ingenuity of policy and management.

Much of the demand for outdoor recreation land can be met by stepping up the use of national, state, and private forests for this purpose through investment in access roads, parking and camping areas, trails, and other facilities. One can choose locations that will be accessible to urban dwellers and at the same time minimize the sacrifice of timber or mineral production. The recreational use of forests usually complements other purposes such as watershed protection. With proper safeguards, some range land and even farm land near cities may also be used for recreation.

The techniques of urban land use planning can help bring about a more efficient and an aesthetically pleasing pattern, with increased emphasis on reservation of parks, nature areas, farm land, and open spaces separating built-up portions. Great, wide strips of megalopolis—Boston to Washington, Pittsburgh to Milwaukee, perhaps San Francisco to Los Angeles—can be planned for multiple purposes including urban living, industry and commerce, outdoor recreation, transportation facilities, and even some agriculture and forestry. Planning of this kind will, of course, require firm public support.

Prospective shortage of forest products. Limitations of domestic supply are more likely to be a barrier to meeting projected demand for forest products and services than for any other major category of resource materials. It is not easy to see how very many additional acres can be shifted into forest production. The solution, so far as it involves the increase of supply, will have to be sought chiefly through improvements on existing forest land.

A greater concentration of cutting on the mature stands in the West will be helpful over the coming twenty years or so, combined with strenuous efforts to improve and upgrade the more rapidly growing stands in the East.

Reduction of losses from insects, disease, fire, and other causes would add greatly to timber production. Direct annual losses from such damage amount to about a quarter of the total cut, and the further losses of growth that otherwise would have taken place are more than twice as large as the actual timber mortality.

Much of the commercial and potentially commercial forest land of the nation is in small farms and other holdings in the South and East. On most of these farms there is little or no incentive for the practice of good forestry. Stronger incentives could materially increase output of timber. Possible ways of accomplishing this include new forms of consolidated management, more suitable types of credit, insurance against losses, tax arrangements that would discourage premature cutting, and aid in reforestation.

For the very long pull, research and experimentation through genetics and physiology may lead to hybrids which will produce marketable timber faster than present trees do. Further efforts to make use of species, sizes, and wood material now left behind in the forests can also make a contribution. So can technological improvements that would make it profitable to use eastern hardwoods for pulp on a much larger scale than at present.

Development of water resources. The nation's chief water problems are shortage of supply in the West and deterioration of quality in the East.

In the West, there are some ways to increase dependable supplies through reservoir construction, measures to control useless plants that are heavy consumers of water, reduction of losses from reservoirs and canals, and watershed management in general. But there are limits to what can be accomplished by such means. Much of the answer, therefore, lies in making better use of the limited supply by policies that channel larger proportions to uses that bring the larger economic benefits—use by cities and industries and sometimes recreational use as well—and smaller shares to the lower-value uses in irrigation agriculture. Social, economic, and legal problems will be encountered in taking action to facilitate such a shift. A movement toward pricing water more in accord with the full cost of developing supplies, preparing them for use, and distributing them could do a great deal to conserve all along the line, from the irrigated field and the factory to the family sink and shower.

The problem in the East is primarily one of improving the management and use of water rather than augmenting total supply. The greatest need is for preventing and abating water pollution. Anti-pollution programs will have to be intensified and carried out over wide geographical areas, frequently on an interstate scale, as in the case of the Ohio River Valley and a number of other basins. Water quality standards need further definition for various uses and various locations.

Good quality fresh water will be wanted in large quantities for outdoor recreation. Supplying it will require compromise and reconciliation with other major uses. For example, the largest number of water recreation facilities will be needed in or near metropolitan centers for convenience of users, yet those are the areas where withdrawal requirements and needs for flow to dilute pollution also tend to be concentrated. Planning to restrict water polluting activities to certain areas would be helpful, as would the strict designation of certain areas for outdoor recreation. Charges could be levied against identifiable polluters of water.

Impact on particular industries and areas.   New technology, product substitutions, new resource discoveries, depletion of older sources, changes in foreign trade policy, and other shifts in the world scene often are hard on particular industries or geographic areas. The coal industry and producing areas are hurt by substitution of other fuels. Mining areas in the West are abandoned when the richer mineral veins are worked out. Cut-over forest areas become depressed. Although farm employment has dropped by nearly 40 per cent during the past thirty years, the increase in agricultural productivity has been so great that particularly in certain areas there are still many more people on farms than can find a reasonably good level of living.

In a relatively free and flexible economy, such as that of the United States, such problems inevitably accompany growth and change. To a large extent they can be handled by maintaining a growing, prosperous economy generally over the country so that displaced workers, managers, and enterprisers can find satisfactory opportunities elsewhere. Beyond this, special efforts are usually desirable to ease and promote necessary transitions, to minimize individual and social damage, and to direct aid especially to those most seriously hurt. Usually this kind of assistance will require positive efforts to retrain and relocate displaced workers, to help adversely affected industries to diversify their activities, and to promote the establishment of new enterprises which can prosper in the the areas undergoing these transitions. This kind of solicitude for disadvantaged industrial, agricultural, and labor groups is justified by reasons of social welfare and fairness to individuals, but only if it can be progressively diminished over a few years. Programs ostensibly designed to serve these purposes sometimes are installed and maintained for other reasons —for example, to perpetuate a special position or privilege long after the need for it has disappeared. An economic system which aims to be competitive within its own national boundaries, and on a world scale as well, must not allow particular segments to receive permanent protection from the changes that competition dictates.

Short-term vs. long-term resource policies. As the projections in this study suggest, the short-term prospects for some resources are quite different from the longer-run outlook. In such instances, one must take care that programs and policies to improve the immediate situation do not unnecessarily aggravate the longer-run problems expected to arise later. For example, with an outlook for surplus production of most basic crops for the next decade or two, a shift in the relative emphasis in soil conservation would appear to be in order. Practices from which the gains in output could be deferred should be preferred to practices whose main effects would be to increase output in the next few years. Soil conservation activities thus become a kind of long-term insurance against increased requirements for farm products in the more distant future. Similarly, present emphasis on basic research in agriculture would be desirable, even though the returns will not come until well into the future.

Other projections underline the increasing significance of nuclear energy during the last two decades of this century. Since for the next two decades conventional sources should suffice to meet demand in all applications without cost increases, research and development need not bear down on immediate commercial feasibility. On the contrary, promising alternative types of fission reactors can be investigated and more basic research can be concentrated on nuclear fusion possibilities.

Quality of the environment. In contrast to the supply of resource materials, where problems will be the exception rather than the rule, maintaining and improving the quality of land and water resources will become of increasing concern. Broadly speaking, this question of the natural environment is one of pleasant surroundings, although health and comfort are also involved. For the most part, the problems of environment are pretty much beyond the range of economics; for usually the dollar costs and benefits are still unmeasurable and many may remain so. However, there is here a wide field for imaginative exploration and research by economists.

The preservation of scenic beauty and the improvement of recreational areas beyond what might result from good business practices present important problems of this kind. So does the need for care and discrimination in the use of pesticides which may exterminate wildlife. Polluted water and air often bring two kinds of trouble: they not only bring ugliness and discomfort but also they may burden whole cities and severely limit future growth and improvement. The balancing of private and social responsibilities in these matters is difficult, not only because of the lack of a coincidence between those who cause the pollution or disfigurement and those who are harmed by it, but also because of the scale and cost of prevention and abatement programs. For the future the quality of growth—the aesthetics of resource use—will be as much a part of the standard of living as the sheer amounts of things to be consumed—probably more so as people's appetite for material goods becomes more nearly satiated. Policy decisions on such problems will usually be more "political"—that is, settled by vote or other public action at national, state, or local levels—than on those resource policy decisions in which the operations of the marketplace play a large part. But social scientists are likely to come increasingly to grips with problems of resource quality, as they seek to provide sounder bases for decisions.

Resource policies and national policies. Resource policies are not sufficient unto themselves; they operate in conjunction with other policies across the whole range of national concerns. Thus, resource policies at many points ought to be integrated with public works policy, tax and subsidy policy, transportation policy, foreign trade policy, military policy, and so on. Making resources policies pull together with policies in these other fields is a difficult undertaking, analytically and administratively, and calls for improved processes of policy formulation, operation, and evaluation.

Many examples of the importance of policy consistency can readily be found. Oil is one. Among the considerations that constrain the working out of the principles of least cost are national security, relations with particular other countries, solicitude for the domestic industry, concern for short-run business stability, and development of subnational regions. The constructive resolution of these conflicting aspects requires the highest order of statecraft. Policy objectives have to be cast in a broader frame than resources, or anything else, alone; techniques and processes of reconciliation become a necessity. Another example would be inland waterway transportation policy, which is a part of national transportation policy involving rail, highway, air, and pipeline transport as well as water.

Whatever specific resource policy may be under consideration, it should be tested and evaluated not only against broad objectives for resource policy but also against objectives in surrounding fields of policy.

In both government and industry the processes by which policies are made—political, consultative, budgeting, competitive, and bargaining processes—require most careful attention if good results are to be secured.

There can of course be no single monolithic Resource Policy. In fact, even a single water policy or energy policy would have to be stated in such general terms as to be rather useless. Policies, like actions, tend to come in bits and pieces, never thoroughly consistent in their direction. The real task is to make them more consistent, to fit them more to a well-conceived pattern. Clearly established general objectives and well-designed processes of policy debate and formulation, plus systematic review and evaluation, offer the best guarantee of policy improvements.

The Challenge and the Opportunity

The rest of the twentieth century affords the prospect of sustained economic growth in the United States supported by an adequacy of resource materials—*provided* technologic advances and economic adaptation of them continue, *provided* foreign sources of raw materials remain open through maintenance of a viable world trading and investing system, and *provided* government resource policies and private management of resource enterprises improve in farsightedness, flexibility, and consistency. Each of these provisos presents difficulties—and opportunities—well within the capacity of research, policy, and action to deal with successfully.

We Americans rather pride ourselves on our initiative, and on the fact that throughout our history we have behaved as if we were the masters of our fate and not passive tools of blind economic force. The generally optimistic conclusions of this study rest on the belief that Americans over the next four decades will be no less clear-sighted and self-reliant—that they will recognize the things that need to be done to assure the continuing adequacy of resources and then go ahead and do them.

Index

251

RELATED RFF PUBLICATIONS

The Parent Study

Resources in America's Future: Patterns of Requirements and Availabilities, 1960–2000. Hans H. Landsberg, Leonard L. Fischman, Joseph L. Fisher. 1963. Baltimore: The Johns Hopkins Press. 1,040 pp. $15.00.

Background Studies in Depth

Although research on Resources in America's Future drew upon a wide variety of sources, a handful of detailed RFF studies were particularly useful in their respective fields. These books, all published for RFF by The Johns Hopkins Press, are:

Scarcity and Growth: The Economics of Natural Resource Availability. Harold J. Barnett and Chandler Morse. 1963. 320 pp. $5.50.

Trends in Natural Resource Commodities: Statistics of Prices, Output, Consumption, Foreign Trade, and Employment in the United States, 1870–1957. Neal Potter and Francis T. Christy, Jr. 1962. 580 pp. $17.50.

Energy in the American Economy, 1850–1975. Sam H. Schurr and Bruce C. Netschert, with Vera F. Eliasberg, Joseph Lerner, and Hans H. Landsberg. 1960. 796 pp. $12.50.

259

Regions, Resources, and Economic Growth. Harvey S. Perloff, Edgar S. Dunn, Jr., Eric E. Lampard, and Richard F. Muth. 1960. 760 pp. $12.00.

Land for the Future. Marion Clawson, R. Burnell Held, and Charles H. Stoddard. 1960. 672 pp. $8.50.

PAPERBACK BOOKS FOR STUDENTS AND GENERAL READERS

Land for Americans. Marion Clawson. Chicago: Rand McNally and Company. 1963. 152 pp. $2.25. (Based on *Land for the Future.*)

Land and Water for Recreation. Marion Clawson. Chicago: Rand McNally and Company. 1963. 160 pp. $2.25.

Minerals and Men. James F. McDivitt. Baltimore: The Johns Hopkins Press. 168 pp. $1.95.

How a Region Grows: Area Development in the U.S. Economy. Harvey S. Perloff, with Vera W. Dodds. New York: Committee for Economic Development [Supplementary Paper No. 17]. 1963. 148 pp. $2.25. (Based on *Regions, Resources, and Economic Growth.*)

NATURAL RESOURCES FOR U.S. GROWTH
A Look Ahead to the Year 2000
by Hans H. Landsberg

designer:	Edward D. King
typesetter:	Monotype Composition Company
typeface:	Fairfield
printer:	The Murray Printing Co.
paper:	Warren's 1854
binder:	The Murray Printing Co.